A Doctor's Life

*A tale of love and medicine from
a hospital and family doctor
in the 1940s and 1950s*

Dr Robert Clifford

FOR my LOVEY NEIGHBOUR
Sarah,
will all good wishes
Bob Cooper
(P-Robert Clifford)

YMAS 2015

Copyright © Dr Robert Clifford 2015

Published by Corazon Books
(Wyndham Media Ltd)
27, Old Gloucester Street, London WC1N 3AX
www.greatstorieswithheart.com

ISBN:190975224X
ISBN-13:978-1909752245

Dedication

This small book is dedicated to the doctors, nurses and staff of Derriford Hospital, Plymouth, Devon who, by their skills, dedication and patience have given me extra precious years of life.

PROLOGUE

THE BEVIN BOY

To say that there was tension in the pit cage was one of the greatest understatements of all time. Already, one of the ten men in it had become incontinent of urine in a corner of the cage.

No miner ever liked the gravitational half mile drop from the surface to the pit bottom. As it slowed down in its descent, and approached the pit bottom, it felt as if you were going up again.

On this particular day, having almost reached the bottom, it jerkily went back up and stopped halfway, a quarter of a mile from the bottom and a quarter of a mile from the surface. There was no means of contacting anyone to find out what was happening.

This was 1945. Most of the other nine miners thought that they might die. I was different. I knew that I was going to die. I was familiar with this situation. My father, in the climb up his career ladder, had for a few years been the Chief Electrical Engineer to the Kent coalfield. His deputy was a small, quiet man whose life was his wife and three young daughters.

One day he and my father were due to go down the pit and inspect some machinery. They reached the pit cage when my father realised that he needed something extra to take down. So he said to his deputy, 'You go down on this draw and I will come down on the next.' The deputy got into the cage on his own and it shot off down in its descent.

What no-one realised was that the cage had got stuck halfway, but the steel cable by which it was suspended continued to be wound down from the big winding wheel, piling more and more steel cable on the cage top. Only the deputy electrical engineer was aware of what was happening and what was going to happen. After a sufficient weight of cable had piled on top of the cage it made the whole thing come crashing down to the bottom, killing him.

Nobody spoke. The only sound was a leaky compressed air pipe hissing away, and the sound of men passing water. It could not have been just one man; the first must have started the others off. I remember that in the school boxing championships I was so busy rushing to spend pennies before a fight that I got quite exhausted and was beaten on points by an opponent I should really have beaten easily. I have absolutely no idea how long we had been in the cage; in this situation time certainly stood still. It was probably at least half an hour; it felt like days. It was not uncommon for the cage to go up again for a minute – but nothing like this.

Knowing what was going to happen, I ran through my mind all the things I should have done and hadn't, and all the things that I shouldn't have done which I had, and it was a pretty unhealthy balance.

I was trying to catch the noise of the steel cable piling on top of the cage, but with the noise of the leaking compressed air pipe and passing water in the cage, I could not hear anything else. Then, after however long we had been there, suddenly the cage began to slowly descend to the pit bottom and we all got out.

I understand that three or four occupants of the cage did not come down the pit again for a couple of weeks. One never came down again.

Nowadays this would be called post-traumatic stress syndrome but the term had not been invented then. There was never any explanation as to why that happened to the cage that day.

Thank God it never happened again in my time underground.

I was a collier; that is to say I was one of the ten per cent of miners who actually worked at the coalface. The name of our colliery was Burkit; as you can probably imagine, miners working at other collieries, when talking about Burkit, often replaced the 'k' for 'sh'.

I worked on the Nine Face, which was three miles out from the pit bottom. I travelled the first two miles to Three Face on a Paddy Train, which had open carriages. The main hazard was that some of the older miners still chewed tobacco, and if you get a bit of tobacco spit in your eye it certainly wakes you up. So I usually kept my eyes shut as we travelled, which was not difficult as I had to get up each morning at 4.00 a.m. to catch the 4.15 a.m. pit bus, six days a week.

We walked up the last mile to the coalface, along what was known as a Supply Gate. As the name implies, it was one of two tunnels that took supplies up to the coalface; and then there was the Main Gate, which was in the middle of the other two, with its huge conveyor belt that took coal away from the coalface to go on into pit tubs and be transported on and up to the surface.

Nine Face was 300 yards long and three-foot six to

four feet thick; a sandwich of coal between a rock ceiling and rock floor. That, of course, is not standing room but it was considered an ideal height, because although you couldn't stand up straight, it was great for shovelling.

On the night shift the coalface was undercut to a depth of six feet with a type of chainsaw on a very heavy machine, then the face conveyor belts moved to a position about three feet from the coal. Taking great care, a hole was drilled in the face every twelve yards and, taking even more care still, a shot – an explosive charge – was put into the hole and the coal was blown out. Hopefully it would clear the coal to the back of where it had been cut. Most often, unfortunately, what was known as a breaking-in shot did not work properly and a collier would have to come with his pick and hack his way right through to the back of the cut. He could then make it much easier peeling coal off the front and manoeuvring with a crow bar and shovelling it onto the conveyor belt.

The twelve yards distance between the two breaking shots was called a stint and your job was to clear the coal from the stint – that was about twelve tons of coal. Very often I could not see the man in the next stint until he got his coal clear. We then had to timber. When I say 'timber', it was metal roof bars and metal props; timber props in Burkit Colliery had long since been forgotten.

My stint was stint number twelve, between the two Willies – Willie Shufflebottom in number eleven was a thick-set Yorkshire man who worked slowly but somehow seemed to finish his stint before I did. He was a staunch Salvation Army man and did not like crude pit talk, but in spite of that was pleasant enough. As opposed to Willie Wales in stint fourteen who was a Jack the Lad; the Errol Flynn of Burkit. He was known as 'Canary Wales', as he sang all the time he worked and he bred canaries, which were big in 1945, particularly in Burkit.

There were few households without canaries, including the family I lodged with; John and Elsie Davis. Elsie had a canary called Bobby, which she talked to all day, and if he made some sort of noise back, she thought she could interpret it and would say, 'Fancy him saying that!' when probably all he'd done was pass some wind.

There were two canaries, called Jack and Jim, in the pit bottom office of the underground quartermaster. It was rumoured that he was in love with them. An egg was found in their cage. This caused a huge amount of laughter and leg pulling from the rest of the miners. For weeks they used to mutter, 'Dirty old bugger!' as they walked past his office, and he got more and more frustrated. Of course, almost certainly, Canary Wales had slipped an egg in when nobody was looking.

Canaries were vital for testing the air, when there had been explosions in pits, or roof falls. If you were going to unexplored places that you weren't sure were ventilated properly and the canaries fell dead when you got there, then you knew it wasn't a good place to be. These two old canaries, Jack and Jim, were almost in retirement. Burkit was such a good and well-ventilated pit that I doubt if there were any breathing apparatus sets down at the pit bottom. But these two little birds were chugging on into old age.

Sitting with Canary one day in the pit canteen, the girl serving dinner seemed ashamed to serve us and looked embarrassed as she did so.

'What's the matter with her?' I asked.

'Oh, I shagged her last night,' said Canary.

'How many of the girls have you made love to?'

'I haven't made love to anyone; I have just shagged six or seven.'

'What's the girl at the till waving at you for?'

'Oh it's her turn this weekend,' said Canary.

'What does your wife think?'

'Oh,' he said, 'she's used to it; it keeps her on her toes.'

As we were speaking a grey-haired, rather stooped cleaning lady passed us sweeping the floor – as she passed Canary there was a sort of snort of disgust.

'Oh no, surely not?' I said.

'Oh yes, a year last Christmas,' he said. 'She said it was the best Christmas she ever had.'

He was incorrigible, but you could not help liking him. I often used to find my stint was a bit too much for me and it was always Canary Wales who helped me out; never the parsimonious Willie Shufflebottom.

The truth was that I was not a genuine collier; I was an embryo doctor working down a coal mine and although the limit of my actual medical knowledge was having dissected a dogfish and a rabbit, everyone referred to me as 'Dr Bob'. I was always in demand for medical problems or medical advice, which of course I always gave.

What had happened was that in December 1944 I passed my First MB; the first step on the medical ladder, and was destined for medical school. I had, by now, thought that I wanted to do something before I went to medical school. I pondered and thought that a year down a coal mine might be just the experience that would help me when I became a General Practitioner, which was what I hoped to be. My grandfather had been a coal miner.

I rang the Coal Board who, to my surprise, said they would be delighted to have me for a year. They sent forms to me. I was to be part of the Bevin Boys scheme. In 1943, with only three weeks' supply of coal left in the country, Ernest Bevin brought in the scheme that ten per cent of all conscripts, instead of going into the Army,

Air force or Navy, had to go and work down the mines.

As a potential medical student, I was exempt. I had notice to report to the Training Coal Mine near Sheffield in late February 1945. My father saw me off.

I reported to my Nissan Hut Encampment and I was determined to make the most of my year as a miner. I had a month at my training pit and was later billeted out to Burkit, to John and Elsie Davis as a lodger. At the beginning I not only had to share the lodgings with a fellow billitee, I had to share a double bed with someone I did not know.

My first bed mate was a redundant sheet metal worker from Birmingham who had both a sweet shop and a wife and two children. He couldn't believe where he was. He used to cry each night as he said his prayers on his side of the bed. He managed to get discharged in a couple of weeks on health grounds. He was followed by a public schoolboy from Sedbergh. He was even more horrified to find himself in this situation. The final straw was when he found he had a flea. By pulling strings, he quickly managed to get into the army. From then on, I had the bed to myself.

The Davis house was a two-bedroomed, semi-detached house with a main living room where there was an iron multi-purpose coal burner stove, which was kept alight day and night through the year. There was a shed where John kept his pride and joy – a motorcycle and sidecar. Plump Elsie had swollen legs and sometimes found it difficult to get into the side car. Knowing that I had medical inclinations, she confided to me that she had phlebitis and could be 'taken' at any time.

They looked after me well; high tea at 5.30 pm, then at 9.00 pm either John or I went to the chip shop for fish and chips, mushy peas and occasionally scratchings.

There was a large coal bunker next to John's motorbike shed and once a month I would help him bring in the free ton of coal that was tipped onto the pavement outside. Down the pit, I did a month on the haulage, and then two months as a coalface borer, which was a bit of a nightmare – scrambling up and down the coalface with a six-foot compressed air drill, at everybody's beck and call. Until one day the overman (underground manager) said, 'Dr Bob, you've been wanting to be a proper collier; there is a place on Nine Face between the two Willies.'

I wasn't sure what that meant until I found that it was the stint between Willie Shufflebottom and Willie Wales. Getting a stint of coal off and doing your own timbering, with metal props and babs, was sheer hard graft. I would be down the pit about 5.30 a.m. on my stint about 6.00 a.m., and then back up at 3.00 p.m. to have a really good, subsidised meal in the pit canteen. I did not take food onto the coalface with me; just a five-pint oval-shaped tin of water called a Dudley – I could have drunk double. All I wore was a pair of cotton shorts, my safety boots, and my safety helmet, and we had hand lights; battery lights – a bit like small lighthouses.

I thought that William Shufflebottom, at forty years old, was an old man, and William Wales middle-aged – he was thirty. I was eighteen, fit and robust but coalface work was different.

Working at the coalface was a physical challenge every day. In quieter moments on the face you could hear Canary Wales singing, with his thin, reedy voice. I said to him once, 'You seem to sing falsetto; have you been castrated?'

'No,' he said laughing, 'the funny thing is that many have suggested I ought to be.' He was such a great character and was a sort of father figure to me.

Being far out, we often passed disused roadways as we walked down to the Paddy Train. The roadways had been access routes to worked-out coalfaces. They were blocked off with flimsy barricades with 'Keep Out' notices on them. These were definitely not safe. From time to time Canary Wales would say, 'Come on Dr Bob, let's have a look down here.'

It was quite dangerous as they were not maintained nor well-ventilated like the rest of the colliery, and the roof had come down in some. But Canary would lift up the barricade and we would walk down the dusty tunnel keeping our eyes open for little sandy trickles coming from the roof that indicated that it, or part of it, might be about to fall.

'What are we looking for, Canary?' I asked.

His standard reply was, 'Anything that might turn up.' He was always showing me little things he had picked up outside the pit. Some were quite valuable.

I said, 'Did any of these fall off the back of a lorry?'

'It is possible,' he replied, laughing. 'I can't remember.'

I could not think of anything of value that might turn up in these disused tunnels. I am sure he was after something, but never understood what.

I had been on the coalface for about four months when I had a call to the manager's office; I could not understand this. I went up to his office, knocked on the door and follow his instruction to 'come in'.

'Sit down lad,' he said. 'I have just heard from the Ministry of Labour that you are officially classified now as a Bevin Boy.'

'Good,' I said.

'Just a minute, before you get too excited; this means that instead of finishing here in four to five months, this is your National Service and you have another two years before you are discharged. Do you want me to move you to haulage?'

'No,' I said, 'I would like to stay where I am.'

'Good lad!' he said, and the interview was over.

In a way it was a relief; many of the Bevin Boys were good friends and I always felt uneasy when talking to them. None of them wanted to be down a coal mine and they would have to do two and a half years, and I, 'Mr Medical Student', was only down for a year. I was no more a medical student than the colliery cat! Sometimes things work out for the good. When I was eventually discharged, I was classified as an ex-serviceman, had my medical school fees paid, and got a living allowance.

When I told Canary, he said, 'I hope you're not too disappointed. You did stand out a bit in a crowd. I enjoy your company and these tunnels are a bit dangerous if you're on your own.'

I replied, 'They *are* dangerous – full stop.'

'Never mind,' said Canary, grinning, 'goodness knows what we might find.'

John and Elsie were delighted to hear my news; for them I was the son they never had.

So life went on.

Canary became a great friend; the only thing that I did not like about our relationship was having from time to time to accompany him down those old roadways. I used to go to the Miners' Institute with him and several times went to his house for a meal. His wife was a lovely lady and much younger than him. He did say one day that he could 'fit me up with a bit of crumpet', but I declined.

The months seemed to tick by; Christmas came and Elsie pointed to a teacup and said, 'Try that,' with a smile. She had put a wallop of gin into a cup of tea. It was awful! I just had to force it down and look cheerful, otherwise it would have taken all the fun away.

I was part of pit life by now and took to work as the daily routine. Then the five-day week started. I was never sure whether this was the time that coal mines were nationalised. It was a huge change of life. If you worked five shifts you were paid for six; if you only did four you were only paid for four.

The great joy of having the whole of Saturday and Sunday off was incredible. Canary and I went off to football and rugby games, and a few times to the dog track. During Pit Week (the holiday week) the three of us, Canary, his wife and I, went to Blackpool and stayed in a boarding house and enjoyed the fun of the fair.

At the fair we went on the Big Dipper and a thing called the Octopus, which made us all sick, having been whirled around and around all over the place. At night we went to the Tower Ballroom with its Wurlitzer organ; we danced – me with Mary Wales, whilst Canary shot around as if he were recruiting talent for a talent show, which he probably was.

'Just look at him,' said Mary Wales. 'He doesn't change, but I can't stop loving him.'

'Yes,' I said, 'he is a bit special.'

Back at work the routine continued. There is something special about colliers; they were the most decent lot of men I have ever met. On the coalface you were only as safe as the least safe collier and no one ever let the others down.

Much as I liked them all, the time was looming when I would be leaving and going to medical school. I started to apply for a place. I tried Sheffield, Nottingham and Leeds. No go. So I thought I would have a go at a London teaching hospital. I went down to Paddington to St Mary's Hospital – the nearest teaching hospital to the station. They seemed much more interested in my being a coal miner and having been good at rugby at school than anything else. I was interviewed by three different people, and then was called in by the Hospital Secretary who said, 'You will be pleased to know that you have been accepted and there will be a place for you as soon as you are discharged.'

'Yipee!'

I could not wait to get back to Burkit and tell everybody. Coming to London meant that I had been away two nights. The next morning I was impatient with the train, to hurry north, and more impatient with the bus from Sheffield to Burkit.

As the bus travelled past the colliery I could see a crowd of people waiting round the pithead. Something had gone wrong. I rushed straight from the bus to the pit.

'What's wrong?' I asked the nearest man in the crowd.

'Oh,' he said, 'Canary is missing.'

I rushed across to get my underground gear and went back to the pit top and said, 'I want to go down, I know where he'll be – down one of his bloody disused roadways.'

I set off with a couple of other colliers and we explored disused roadway after disused roadway. No sign of a rock fall, or Canary. Then we found a little one I had been unaware of before. It was narrow to start with then after a while, it broadened out. I was a bit light-headed; we had been rushing to and fro and I had had no food that day. We went along this tunnel and rounded a large bend; there was no sign of a rock fall, but finally there, in the distance, we could see Canary fast asleep.

'Let's go and wake the bugger up,' said one of the colliers.

As I had been getting light-headed some instinct made me shout, 'No, let's get out of here and ring the Pit Bottom for the canaries.'

They were an age coming; when they did arrive, Jack and Jim seemed to be pleased with this trip out. We made our way cautiously along the roadway, with me carrying the cage, to the point we had reached before. 'Okay,' I said, 'let's have a look at Jack and Jim.'

We took the cloth off the cage to see that both were

flat out on the bottom of the cage.

'Quick, let's get out of this tunnel.'

So we shot back to the main well-ventilated roadway, but Jack and Jim did not revive. They had done their job and saved us from getting gassed.

It took a rescue team with breathing apparatus to go and fetch Canary's body. He had a massive funeral, with Jack and Jim buried with him. Strangely, many of the mourners were women.

With Canary Wales gone it was like the lights going out, and work from then on was just sheer hard graft. Mary Wales was completely devastated. She expected me to call every day. For a time I did, and then I tried to wean her off me. We reached a stage where she said, 'Couldn't we start going out together on Saturday afternoons?' Fortunately, I had just joined a local rugby club and was genuinely booked each Saturday afternoon. Knowing that rugby was important at the hospital, I wanted to hone my skills before I started there.

I did not see Mary Wales for some time but, happily, one day on a bus to a rugby match I saw her walking along on the arm of a man of the same age. I was delighted.

Eventually I had finished my last stint and after a weeping 'Goodbye' from Elsie, and a tight-lipped one from John, I caught the train to London.

My father picked me up from the station in London, closing one chapter of my life, and with building excitement I was looking forward to the next.

CHAPTER ONE

FIRST SIGHTS

I stood in the entrance hallway of the medical school student accommodation. It was my first day. I could not ever remember being so happy. I was on my way; hoping to become a doctor. As I had done my National Service, I thought that I might be a couple of years older than most students, and so it proved. I had come early so that I could see what the rest of my year looked like. My room was F5, one of the small apartments in a cul-de-sac of six, with shared facilities for cooking, laundry and showering. I had met four of the six so far – all from minor public schools, but all quite nice without too much pretence. I was on the lookout for F6.

As I had been standing there for quite some time, questioning and being questioned by people about their room numbers, it was assumed that I was part of the staff and, as I now had a pretty good idea about the layout – it was all alphabetical – I could usually point people in the right direction.

One very ostentatious young man with a silk waistcoat bounded in and came up to me saying, 'Apartment room A4?'

I replied, 'It's the furthest group of rooms, right down at the far end of the accommodation. It sounds like a main road.'

He said, 'I don't want any lip from you. Just pick up those bags and take them down. I have one in the car, I'll bring it in then you can take it down too.'

I asked, 'Are you injured or in pain or something?'

His face grew red. 'Do as I say,' he said, 'or I'll get you the sack!'

'From where?'

'From here,' he said in a loud voice.

'I don't work here.'

'Well, what are you doing here?'

'I'm a medical student, like you.'

'You look older than most of us.'

'Yes, I've already done my National Service, before rather than after.'

'Oh,' he said, looking deflated and so very young – seventeen or eighteen.

'Come on.' I picked up two of the cases. 'I'll take these two cases, you fetch the other one.'

'Thanks.'

So I trundled down with his two cases. I passed him on the way back looking even younger and a bit scared.

'Sorry,' he said.

'That's okay, you don't want to be making enemies on the first day.' I held out my hand. 'My name's Bob Ramsden.'

'My name's George Hinkley-Hamilton,' and we shook hands. 'I hope we will be friends.'

'Of course we will; it's a big wide world out there. I'll look out for you.'

'Thanks,' he said, and there was a small tear in his eye.

I made my way back to the front hallway, still on the lookout for F6, when a luxury limousine drew up.

An extremely smart, middle-aged man got out, accompanied by the most beautiful, immaculately dressed girl – presumably his daughter. He struggled through the door with two pigskin suitcases that looked very heavy. He came straight to me and said, 'What do we call you, young man?'

I said, 'Bob, sir.'

'Well, Bob, could you direct us to …' then looked at some papers in his hands, '… to apartment E1?'

'Yes sir, it's about ten bays down on the right.'

He said to his daughter, who was inspecting a notice board, 'Priscilla dear, we have to go this way,' indicating the direction I had pointed, and he added, 'I hope Baggage Bob here might give me a hand with the cases. Is that alright with you, Bob?'

'Certainly, sir,' I replied, and picked up the bags, which were quite heavy. I didn't mind walking behind this lovely young girl; she looked just about as good from the back as she did from the front. When we arrived at her apartment he took the bags from me and put them in her room. 'Just hang on, Bob, I'll be with you in a minute.' When he came out he asked, reaching for his wallet, 'What am I in your debt, Bob?'

'Nothing, I'm a medical student, not actually a bag handler.'

He put his hand on my shoulder. 'My dear boy, I do apologise, you just seemed a bit older than most here.'

'Yes, I got my National Service out of the way before I came here.'

'I see. What were you in? The Army, Air Force or Navy?'

'I was a coal miner.'

'Good for you. What did you do down the mine?'

'I was a collier – a pick and shovel man at the

coalface for over two years.'

'That must have been tough for you?'

'No, it was a privilege. They were the most decent lot of men I have ever met.'

'I know exactly what you mean. There was a group of them in my platoon at Arnhem. They were the steadiest of the lot. Sadly they were all killed. It was all pretty awful.'

'I'm sorry. Were you taken prisoner?'

'Yes, Bob, but I don't like to talk about it,' he said, holding out his hand. 'I am Miles Justin-Boyston.'

'Is it Sir Miles Justin-Boyston?'

'Yes, how on earth did you know that?'

'I didn't, I just thought that you looked like a Sir, sir.' He smiled. 'You are Bob …?'

I replied, 'Bob Ramsden,' and we shook hands.

'Which direction do you want to go, Bob?'

'I want to be a GP.'

'I think you are made for it. Priscilla wants to be a neurologist. Hang on, you must meet her.' He knocked on the door. 'Priscilla, come and meet a fellow student.'

She came out and I was completely stunned. Everything about her was beautiful and elegant. She had a quality I could not express; she looked as if she exuded loveliness within and without. Good breeding shone through. Having given up religion some years ago, here was someone I could really worship.

'This is Bob; he was a coal miner.'

'That sounds interesting,' she said, putting her hand out. We had a proper handshake and I felt I had been hit by static electricity; I wanted to hang on to her hand. 'I would be interested to hear about it.'

She really did sound as if she meant it, but perhaps that was just good breeding. I felt the chance of her doing so was very low. The thought of it just being possible was delicious, which is a stupid word to describe what I thought. I could not find the right word. But just at the moment of meeting her I was determined that in my own way I would cherish her.

I was just enjoying being near her when two hysterical girls ran down the corridor screaming, 'Prissy! Prissy!' Her father rolled his eyes.

'Goodbye, dear. Ring if there are any problems. Come on, Bob.' As we walked down the corridor together he explained, 'She is just back from being polished for a year in Switzerland.'

'They seem to have made a good job of it.'

'Yes, but there are too many "Hooray Henrys" about.'

I said, 'But they were girls.'

'Is there a difference?' he replied. 'Bob, I do hope Priscilla will bring you over sometime to have a talk about coal miners. I'm afraid my ancestors were rather beastly to them. It was what our family fortune was based on – "Black Gold".'

'I would love to.'

As we reached the door, he said, 'Bob, I would be grateful if you could keep an eye open for her.'

'Of course, sir. Having met her, I would happily die for her.'

He gave me a strange look. 'Bob, forget about the dying bit. It's much more important to stay alive. And, Bob, I am Miles to you, not Sir Miles.'

'Yes, S... Miles.'

We shook hands and he left.

I tried to get my feet back on the ground and retired to my apartment, where I lay on my bed and attempted to sort out this brief encounter. When I had said to her father I would happily lay my life down for his daughter, I really meant it. I resolved always to keep her in sight as much as possible. She really was the impossible dream.

After an hour's fantasy about Priscilla, I got up and found that F6 was occupied. I went in and introduced myself and discovered, to my delight, that he was a Welsh grammar school boy called Jehoyda Jones, which when pronounced came out as 'Joyda' Jones. We gelled immediately and continued to be friends for the rest of our lives.

As well as the cooking facilities at the apartments, there was a large student restaurant in the medical school, so Joyda and I set off to explore. It contained large bench tables and forms, and could seat about three hundred people. There was a cafeteria, offering a huge range of nourishing and inexpensive foods and, of course, tea, coffee, soft drinks, cakes and biscuits, et cetera. We settled for coffee and cake.

I could see Priscilla sitting at a table across from us with a lot of Hooray Henrys and their female equivalents. She gave a small wave and then must have said something, as the whole table turned to have a look at me. My conversation with Joyda, which was all about rugby, was interrupted by a silk waist-coated Hooray Henry who said, 'Have you any coal on you, old boy?'

I stood up, deliberately stepping on one of his winkle-pickered feet. I was six feet and weighed fifteen stones in those days. 'Sadly not, old man,' I replied. 'But see this fist here? I can place it anywhere you like.'

He was now squeaking. 'You're standing on my foot.'

'Oh dear, why not ring Mummy?'

He was trying to balance on one leg; a small push by Joyda put him on his bottom.

I looked rather sadly at Priscilla, who smiled and put her thumb up, and that made my day. I realised that I was wishing the impossible; she was always surrounded by 'her group' and I certainly was not the only one who yearned for her.

Joyda and I got down to the serious talk about rugby. He was a Welsh schoolboy international playing at either Fly Half or on the wing. The rugby-mad teaching school had probably given him a scholarship, but he never said. He was also the Welsh two hundred yards champion. I was just a plodding Front Row Forward, but we both got straight into the hospital's First XV, which played top class rugby.

The main rugby event of the year for our hospital side was the final of the Hospital Cup. Apparently, we always got to the final, usually against Guys. Both teams had two or three Internationals. There used to be a huge crowd for the final; always some celebrity, and the year before my first, the Queen had come. There were numerous student rags, flour bag fights and fireworks, and some exotic animal to be paraded. As they had had an elephant the previous year to my first final, we tried to repeat it; but the elephants were on heat or in musk or something, and could not be kept apart. So we were offered either two or more.

We eagerly accepted two, then on reflection thought that if the two elephants started mating on the touchline it might take people's eyes off the ball, as it were, so we had to settle for a camel.

We had the hell of a game with Guys: ding-dong all the way. We were two points down and there was only five minutes to go and the ball came to me in our own half. I was off, and for the first time I saw Priscilla's face in the crowd screaming, 'Come on, Bob!' Until that moment I was absolutely knackered. With that brief glance I seemed to be supercharged. I ran, smashing my way towards their touchline. I was all fury and brute force, and tacklers were literally bouncing off me.

It couldn't last.

I was about ten yards from their line when someone hit me like a missile; as I was going down I could hear the thunder of somebody's boots coming up behind me. So I flung out the ball to see it gathered up by Joyda, who had come from the far side of the field like a train, gathered the ball and ran on to touch down between the posts. We had won the game.

I somehow managed to drag my battered body to the after game communal bath, slid into the warm water, and had a look at myself. I looked and felt as if I had been done over by a tank.

Priscilla would never know that it was she, rather than me, who had won the Hospital Cup.

CHAPTER TWO

JOLLY HOCKEY STICKS

I had always got on well with my father. He was a very skilled sketcher; apparently a star at the Sketch Club. He had been incredibly successful at his work. From being the electrical engineer at Silverwood Colliery in Yorkshire, where I was born, he was now the member of the Central Electricity Generating Board responsible for electricity production for England and Wales. He was good at understanding people. He had an Honorary Degree of Master of Engineering from Liverpool University and a CBE from the Queen, as it were. In his spare time he had invented the first blind-deaf aid.

He had one idiosyncrasy; if he was giving away something he no longer needed, he almost wept with emotion. That is how I acquired his old dinner jacket. He pointed out the huge opportunities and entry into all sorts of levels of society I would have. He was almost tearful as he gave it to me. He, of course, was buying a new one.

My father loved to go to the Friday evening 'Discourses' at The Royal Institution in Ablemarle Street. He also hated going anywhere on his own; so if Louise, his second wife, didn't want to, or could not go, if I were free he took me with him. He would send his chauffeur, Hunter, in his limousine (that went with his job) to pick me up, then we would go to my father's luxury flat where he lived with Louise. Hunter had fought in the Korean War and used to regale me with the stories of its horrors. We had become good friends.

I also loved going to the Friday evening Discourses. You had to wear a dinner jacket with a black tie. Before the meeting you were served with coffee and canapés. You promenaded around the gallery, where there were exhibitions of all the work of famous scientists such as Faraday and Humphrey Davy. You had to be in your seat promptly by 9.00 pm and the lecturer would walk in and plunge straight into his lecture. He would have to time it such that during his last sentence, one hour later, the 10.00 pm bell would ping and he would walk out.

Apparently, in Victorian times it was a great social event. It was much treasured now, particularly by me. I remember one on 'Dreaming Time': A professor, whose name I have forgotten, said that the current thinking was that dreaming was the mechanism that allowed you to download your brain's computer. They showed that the deprivation of two hours dreaming time could mentally derange you in a couple of days, and this was the basis of 'brain-washing'. As a control, if you deprived people of deep sleep for two hours but allowed their dreaming time it had no effect on them; and you learned no more from dreams than you would if you raided somebody's dustbin, which of course does tell you something about them.

I was being picked up by Hunter for one Friday evening Discourse. He was holding the door open of whatever limousine he was driving, when Priscilla and two Hooray Henrys pulled up.

Priscilla came up. 'What's all this, Bob?' she asked.

'This is Hunter, my father's chauffeur. We're just off to The Royal Institution. Hunter, this is a fellow student, Priscilla Justin-Boyston.'

'Good evening, ma'am,' said Hunter, tipping his hat. Then he turned to me. 'Master Robert, I do feel you ought not to keep your father waiting.'

I must have looked like a beetroot. When we got in the car I said, 'You bugger, with all this Master Robert stuff.'

Hunter laughed. 'You fancy her; what are you going to do about it?'

'Nothing. She's premier league, I am only the second divisional south.'

'Bollocks!' Hunter replied.

'How dare you say that to Master Robert?'

'All I can say again is – bollocks!' said Hunter, and we laughed.

I somehow never knew how to handle girls. I only ever had one date; that was when I was coal mining. I went to a dance at the Sheffield Town Hall. I could just afford an orange juice in the first interval, and then a trifle in the second interval. I had been dancing most of the evening with a quite good-looking, but rather raw girl. I plucked up the courage and asked, 'Would you like to go to the pictures next week?'

'Yes,' she said. 'The Odeon 6.30 pm on Wednesday. Meet you outside.'

Her name was Emily. I had never been out on a weekday evening before, as I went to work at 4.15 am each morning and had nine hours at the coalface with a pick and shovel. It was no mean undertaking as it was a two-hour bus ride to Sheffield.

Fortunately, it had been payday on the Monday and I

used up all my sweet coupons to buy her a bar of chocolate. It caused a great sensation at The Davis house. Elsie had specially starched my shirt.

I arrived, trembling, at the Odeon about ten past six. I waited until 7.30 pm and she didn't show up. So I came home and gave the chocolate to Elsie.

At medical school, for all functions I would make sure I was working behind the bar; The Rugby Club Ball, The Cricket Ball, the Christmas Ball and the New Year Ball. It suited me to be 'Good old Bob'. At almost every Ball, Priscilla would dance past the bar with some different drip. She looked absolutely gorgeous. I just ached for her. Somehow she must have been conscious of my presence, as she always smiled and gave a little wave.

I so enjoyed myself as a medical student, and being a member of the First XV of what was an elite team. All we top rugby chaps would sit together at a large table in the student restaurant, with long woolly scarves wound round our necks, allowing the other students to pay homage to us. Not only students; unbelievably some of the consultants also came to seek our attention. Did I have a big head over this? Of course I did.

Nobody had ever noticed me before. Priscilla never came near the table, except for once when she came up after the Hospital Cup final and said, 'Well done in the Cup, Bob.' Little did she know that she had inspired the win.

I had little social life being behind the bar. I was also the new secretary of the rugby club and had to arrange transport for seven teams each Saturday. We were a very rugby-orientated medical school.

Looking across the sports notice board, I saw that there were notes for the football club and the ladies' hockey club. Their team notice showed that Priscilla was the captain. Unfortunately, their matches clashed with rugby matches, so I thought I would never see her play.

Then one day I saw the hockey team line-up for the semi-final of the Hospital Ladies' Hockey Cup. It was mid-week. I made my way to see it, of course, with my ostentatious rugby scarf wrapped around my neck. There were not many spectators; they were mainly women and a dozen Hooray Henrys. So I went towards them.

The girls were playing against Bartholomew's Hospital. Priscilla seemed to be taking them on her own. She was here, there and everywhere and, of course, looking elegant and beautiful, as usual. What a treat – I could just gaze at her as she fought what, fairly obviously, was a losing battle. As I approached I could hear the Hooray Henrys shouting, 'Come on, The Ice Maiden.' When I reached them, they of course stepped aside to let this Rugby God with his scarf come through. I said, 'Who is the "Ice Maiden"?'

One said, 'Priscilla.'

'Why the Ice Maiden?'

Another one said, 'We thought if she would thaw out a bit, she would make a good shag.'

There was a silence. Then the realisation dawned that it was not a good thing to say to me. I paused. 'It is a good job her father, Sir Miles, asked me to keep an eye on her.' Then, like a school prefect talking to the junior school I said, 'I do not want to hear that again.'

Just as I said this, Priscilla started a long solo run. I shouted at the top of my voice, 'Come on, Priscilla.' There was a quick glance as if she thought it was one of her team wanting the ball, then she continued on until she was overwhelmed by the Barts' defence. Unlike Priscilla, most of her team were not very good and they were truly thumped out of the Hospital Cup. As they came off, I made sure I was near their exit. As she passed I said, 'Bad luck, Priscilla.'

'Bob, dear,' she replied, 'how nice of you to support us. I nearly passed to you.'

Then she was gone with her team and all my impossible dreams came flooding back.

I had found little difficulty in settling down to the social and athletic side of medical student life. What I had found much more difficult was to settle down to what I had come for, that is, to train to be a doctor. It was with some trepidation I approached the dissection rooms. I had never seen a dead body before; what I encountered was not what I expected. They were shrivelled up, formaldehyde-filled and looked like large dolls. Dissection, I had imagined, would be a bit like watching a butcher carving up joints in his shop; but it was careful grubbing, cutting layers of tissue through a sort of rubbery texture. Each specific layer, which could be tissue paper thin, had to be exposed, and then shown and passed by the anatomy demonstrator (lecturer).

There were four of us called a 'dissection team'. There was Larry, an ex-bomber pilot, Jack an ex-army captain and Harold, Sir Alexander Fleming's nephew, who I think had been in the Navy. They were all much more studious than I was.

They were also sporty. Somehow, Harold and I found ourselves in the hospital boxing team against Oxford University boxing team. They said we had been very carefully matched. I was to fight the university's Ceylonese boxing secretary and Harold was to fight a middleweight called Reg Severn, who had never boxed for the university before. What they had failed to mention was that my opponent was the captain of the Ceylon Olympic Games boxing team and that Reg Severn was the Royal Navy middleweight boxing champion. I only lasted about twenty-five seconds before my opponent put me down, but did better that Harold, who lasted twenty seconds. Harold retired from boxing then. As they were always short I persevered, and in six fights, three each against Oxford and

Cambridge Universities, I won three and lost three. Against Oxford, I narrowly lost on points to a tall West Indian on the day of my grandmother's funeral. But we were given pen knives for being the best fight of the night.

Some of the family had come to watch the fight, expecting two funerals on the same day. My last fight was against Cambridge University, who we thrashed seven-two. *The Evening Standard* wrote, 'The best fight of the evening was Bob Ramsden, St. Mary's Hospital against R. Luckhurst, Cambridge University.' It read, 'Bob Ramsden, after suffering severe punishment in the first two rounds, by accurate left hand hitting in the third round won on points.'

I thought that was the time to retire – on a high. I bumped into Priscilla a few days later. She said, 'Hello, Boxing Champion Bob, thank God I wasn't there. My father was delighted when he read the paper. He said, "That's just what I would have expected from Bob."'

I conceded, 'I have now retired from boxing.'

'Thank goodness for that,' she sighed, relieved, and swept on with her usual trail of admirers. I was puzzled. Why on earth had she worried about me? I realised that the Hooray Henrys did show me more respect than usual.

Back to the Dissection Room. Arriving early one morning I thought, *blow to all this grubbing about business, what about a few bold incisions?* I thought it looked terrific, but was met with fury by fellow dissectors. 'You've buggered up three weeks' work. Just keep your scalpel to yourself.' So I sat back and let them get on with it.

When it came to the arm, I had one of my own which I really enjoyed dissecting. When the demonstrator examined my work he said, 'Fine, Ramsden, if you wanted to sell it at the butchers, but not too good if you are after tissue identification. I got very fond of my arm and knowing that Hunter was going to pick me up, I left a note to say if a Mr Hunter called for me, to send him up to the Dissection Room.

He came in as I worked away, not appearing to flinch. I said, 'Come on you tough Korean veteran, you have seen these before?'

'Yes,' he said, 'we used to have them for breakfast.'

I casually picked up my arm and carried it off and put it in a trunk full of arms, and then Hunter took me off.

Sometime later he told me that on the night after he had been to the Dissection Room, he slept with his arm above his head. When he woke in the morning, he thought the arm across his face was one from the trunk. It took some time to realise it was his own.

The other three were always poring over anatomy books. I meant to, but did not quite get down to it. Then anatomy was over, on to physiology.

The professor of physiology, a little round man with tiny glasses, was noted for never having discovered anything. It was alleged he had a trained grasshopper which would jump on command; then he cut its back legs off and found that whenever he asked it to jump it didn't. His conclusion was that if you cut a grasshopper's back legs off, it stopped its hearing. People always smiled and took it at face value. I do not think that he ever knew what was alleged of him.

I spent even less time studying physiology than I had anatomy. You were also supposed to do some organic chemistry. Someone said that you could learn it in an afternoon. That's all I gave it. Come the examination, I think I probably only got my name right at the top of the paper. Come the organic chemistry practical, there was an examiner walking round with a board, talking to the borderline cases. He came to me and said, 'Write the formula for urea' (one of the simplest) and I couldn't.

'Okay,' he said, 'write any organic formula.' And I couldn't. He said, 'It has been very nice to meet you. I have watched you play rugby. I think it is very likely that we will meet again in six months.

CHAPTER THREE

CLINICAL STUDIES

I am afraid I had neglected my studies. If Priscilla had been in my dissection group when we cut up cadavers I would have taken more notice, but she was not even in our dissection room. So I failed my anatomy and physiology; that put me back six months behind her. The ever-faithful, hyper-bright Joyda gave up most of his summer holiday to coach me and I did manage to stumble through a 'Pass' in the September, so I would now be a clinical student and almost certain to get a medical qualification.

Thirty of us gathered in the main front hall of the hospital. We all wore short 'bum freezer' white coats to distinguish us from fully white-coated doctors. We were all wearing stethoscopes for the first time. One of the young ones said to me, 'This is great! I am actually beginning to feel like a doctor.'

'Good,' I said. 'I feel more like a cabin boy on the Titanic.'

We were all part of the clinical introductory course and moved round as a body. It must have been terrifying for the patients who were being demonstrated to have thirty white monkeys surrounding their bed. I tried to keep at the back of the round, whilst mentally working out seven rugby teams for the next Saturday. One of the first patients to be examined was a quiet young lady with a lump in her breast. The lecturer was demonstrating how to examine a breast. At this stage of my medical life, to stare at a half-naked woman was so embarrassing that I turned my head and let them get on with it, while I continued to muse on the permutations of the compositions of the rugby teams.

Suddenly the lecturer said, 'You, at the back, come and examine this breast.' I looked round to see who was going to be called for this onerous task. Then, *Oh my God*, it was me. I made my way towards this bare-breasted, rather angry-looking woman. With my fingers stuck out, I started to probe the breasts in much the same way I would examine a melon for ripeness. I had not, in fact, touched a female breast since I was breast-fed a couple of decades and a bit before; I had no idea what I was doing, and after a couple of minutes she smacked my fingers away saying, 'That's enough of that!' to the delight of the other twenty-nine students, who were enjoying my discomfort and were muttering things like, 'Sexy bugger!'

Apparently I should have been doing it with the flat of my hand. The lecturer said, 'Are you hoping to qualify as a doctor, Ramsden?'

'Yes, sir.'

'Well, if you get a good offer from rugby league, I should take it.'

And so the day went on. We saw hernias and varicose veins; felt livers; listened to hearts and chests. I made sure that I took notice. The final patient of the day was in a room of her own. We all crowded in. There was a sort of air of respect, which is the best way I can describe it. There, lying on a couch, was the most beautiful blonde, elegant Swedish girl. She could practically have been a Priscilla clone. She exuded elegance, breeding, composure. We were all in awe. She was wearing an immaculate, very expensive suit, spoiled a bit by the fact that her jacket and blouse were off her left shoulder, but made up for by the beautiful slender arm below the strap of her slip, well-manicured nails at the end of shapely fingers. We stood as if in the presence of royalty.

'Now,' said the lecturer, 'I want you all to go and examine Ingrid's left axillae. You don't mind this hairy lot examining you, do you, Ingrid?'

She gave a gentle nod of her head.

Oh God! I thought, *The poor girl!* But when you sign on as a patient in a teaching hospital you get the best expertise and you have to be prepared to be examined by students. That is the deal.

There was no rush to do it, as students went up one by one. They seemed to want to get away as soon as possible – they just shoved their hand up into the girl's left armpit and came away as quickly as possible.

Eventually it was my turn. I was calm. I said, 'I am so sorry you are having to go through this.'

She smiled a little wry smile.

'I think you are very beautiful.'

Another smile. She certainly had heard this before.

'I will be as gentle as I can,' I said, as put my fingers up into her armpit and found a hard lump a bit like a plum stone. 'I have no idea what it is, but I hope they get you better soon and if you are not completely cured by the time I qualify, I will make you better myself,' I added reassuringly.

'Qualify as soon as you can.'

'I'll try. I hope we meet again.'

'I'm sure we will.'

I squeezed her hand and she squeezed mine back. For some unknown reason, I was close to tears. I managed to stumble to the background; a feeling of dread came over me.

The remaining few finished their perfunctory examinations and the lecturer said, 'Thank you, Ingrid.' We moved to the room next door and were then questioned about the diagnosis. All the bright boys gave various answers, then the lecturer asked, 'What is her prognosis ... outlook?'

Nobody answered.

'Well,' he sighed, 'she will be dead in the next nine to twelve months. There is nothing we can do for her.'

There was a stunned silence. Then someone said, 'Does she know?'

The lecturer replied, 'Yes.'

I was only just able to hold back tears. Two of the girls were crying. 'Now,' said the lecturer, 'this is your first clinical day and I have deliberately dropped you in the deep end. Who has been the outstanding student of the day?'

Nobody replied.

'Well, he stands out a mile. It is of course, Bob Ramsden.'

There was laughter. I thought *You Bastard! Stuff medicine! I am going to smack you as soon as we leave the room. Then I'll go.*

The lecturer continued, 'Yes, he made a cock-up this morning, but how did his examination on Ingrid differ from the rest of you?'

There was no reply.

'Well,' he added, 'he treated Ingrid kindly and as a person. For the rest of you, she could have been a slab of meat. Well done, Bob. If you don't go to rugby league, you could have a future in the Citizen's Advice Bureau. Now off you go. See you at 8.00 am.'

I let everybody clear out then had a quiet weep in the corner of the room. Eventually, I made my way out to see Priscilla in animated conversation with the lecturer.

'Bob, dear, I'm sure you know Gerald Clinaton.'

'Yes.' I knew he was Dr Clinaton; I did not know he was called Gerald.

'We all know Bob,' Dr Clinaton smiled. 'The student at all ends of the spectrum today. They have all just had the "Ingrid Experience".'

'I always weep when I think of her. Come on, Bob, I will walk you home.' She took my arm and we set off. 'Gerald and his wife and children are coming over at the weekend. Gerald's father, Major George Clinaton, was in the army with my father. I shouldn't have done, but I asked how you were getting on. He said providing you did not play too much rugby, you would be fine and that he thought that you might get yourself too close to patients and get torn about with their problems.' We walked back to my cul-de-sac, then she squeezed my hand and said, 'Please come and see Father one day.' This was my second hand squeeze of the day; it was almost too much.

As soon as I got into my room I lay on the bed and wept. Priscilla was always the first girl on my mind, but today I was weeping for Ingrid.

I did see Ingrid again. It was almost exactly nine months later when I was doing my pathology course. One of the bodies one day was Ingrid, in her shroud. She still somehow looked as elegant as she did in life. I thought, I can't possibly stay and watch her post-mortem. But I did and it was terrible. Probably for the first time I realised how precious life is. It touched me that with all my mixed emotions on the first day of my clinical introductory course, Priscilla had actually come, taken my arm and walked me home with a final squeeze of my hand. Did that mean she cared for me? Of course not. She was just a real lady, that's how she was. I must stop having these stupid romantic thoughts, and we were two short for the B15 on Saturday.

Fortunately, after going round, mob-handed as it were, in my clinical introductory course, we were split up into 'firms', that is, groups of six who would be attached to the team of a specific consultant. So I had three months with a physician, three months with a surgeon, three months obstetrics with odd bits of pharmacology; eye, nose and throat somehow slotted in. Our six, of course, were mainly rugby players of one grade or another. Although probably one of the top teams, we were not noted for our intellectual ability so did get a bit roughed up by our particular consultant. We had the professor of medicine who headed what was called the medical unit. He had the habit of massaging his right ear lobe when talking; you could always recognise someone from his unit as, to a man, they massaged their ear lobes. He did have a hard job teaching us. But he was very tough with us, and did not spare his criticism. He could shrivel you with a sarcastic look; he was particularly hard on Jock, a massive Scottish trial second row forward, who was doing his clinical course for the second time. We would reach a bedside and then he would order, 'Fetch me a chair.' Then we would stand while he sat on the chair at the patient's bedside and started demonstrating and discussing the case with us. He usually questioned Jock first. It was cruel. I kept out of the firing line as much as possible. We did have a couple of bright sparks in our six who always competed to give answers; some of them obscure. There was one thing that Professor P taught me when one of the bright sparks gave an obscure answer. He said, 'If you look at a telegraph wire with a cluster of birds on it, which do you think they would be, starlings or canaries?' Of course they said, 'Starlings.' Then he said, 'Don't keep on telling me canaries.' I have never forgotten this and often in my medical life it has come to my rescue.

He did muck Jock about too much. I felt that someday something was going to happen, and it did. One day, on reaching a bedside, the usual routine – a chair. 'I'll get it, sir,' said Jock. He went across the ward and picked up a massive seat as if it were a light cane chair, and put it down behind the professor, who sat on it. It was something that you could sit on – it was a commode. We could not help giggling. The professor went on describing the case he was going to show us; then he realised that we were paying less attention than usual. 'What's going on?' he enquired, suddenly becoming aware that what he was sitting on was a commode, not a chair. He became apoplectic. He shouted at Jock, 'How dare you!'

Jock stood eyeball to eyeball with him. 'I'm sorry sir, it just looked so comfortable.' Jock also indicated that just another word from the professor and he would have picked him up and thrown him out of the window.

He yelled, 'You are all hooligans; you don't deserve to be called medical students,' and stormed off.

After our three months he went off to be Professor of Medicine at Oxford University. I never knew whether our team had driven him to despair or whether it was a promotion. What I could confidently predict was that it would not be too long before the whole of Oxford would be massaging their ear lobes when they spoke.

Having completed three months medicine with the same team, we were plunged into surgery. We managed to get on the firm of Mr Jackson-White who was, at the time, the leading surgeon in the country. He was also the president of the rugby and boxing clubs. He would take on anything; often it was failed surgery by other surgeons. He was a nightmare to work for. His House Surgeon and Registrar looked like ghosts. He would start a surgical operating list at 4.00 pm; go away at 7.00 pm; come back at 10.00 pm and operate until 1 am. Then the next morning he would arrive at 8.00 am in a smart pin-striped suit to see his patients of the day before. We all, in turn, had to scrub up, put on green operating gowns and assist him. He was a terror in the theatre, shouting at everybody and throwing instruments about. When I had to assist, it was mainly hanging on to an L-shaped lever called a retractor. They were used to keep incisions open. I was terrified. He would scream, 'For God's sake, Ramsden, pull. You are not pushing in the scrum – you are trying to keep this wound open.'

As president of the rugby club he was a real father-figure, accompanying us on French and Cornish rugby tours and treating us to meals and shows. Six months after his emaciated House Surgeons had finished their jobs, they would receive a handsome cheque from him.

I remember watching him doing a cranial (head) operation. The patient had his neck and head in a sort of suspended halter. He was given a local anaesthetic for an area about a third of the way down the head. Mr Jackson-White made a small incision then sent for an ordinary brace and bit. As he drilled into the skull, he was all the time talking to the patient. It was surreal.

I was glad to finish the surgery stint. It was fascinating, but we were not instructed in the fundamentals of surgery. What was awful was that doing the surgery, I did not have a glimpse of Priscilla for twelve weeks. I had no difficulty conjuring up her image.

My next course was midwifery. Our group stuck together and we went out to a fairly run down maternity hospital near Chiswick. We stayed in a hostel there, where we slept in dormitories and had very indifferent food. We went over to be fitted with full length white coats and the patients called us 'Doctor' but knew perfectly well we were students. Mixed with the midwifery was gynaecology. There would be a row of ladies on narrow couches, naked from the waist down; knees bent and feet in a sort of stirrups. I was glad I was male. We had to do internal examinations. Most of the ladies flinched, but there was one brazen character who said to us each in turn, 'Oh, that was lovely doctor. I hope you will be back,' and we were the ones to be embarrassed.

There was one poor chap not in our team who had some sort of mental hang-up. He was a nephew of one of the consultants. He was a complete loner. Doing one of these internal examinations, his tie went into the patient with his hand. When his hand came out, the tie was still in. The ladies screamed with laughter. The student looked bemused, then yanked his tie out.

There, in time, would be a name for his mental condition. He did somehow qualify the first time, but never lasted more than a day at jobs he went for. He finished up as a farm labourer.

I did not enjoy gynaecology. Midwifery was fun and had happy endings. I was good at this hands-on stuff; easing the baby's head out, checking that the umbilical cord was not round the baby's head; clamping it in two places then cutting it. It was when the anterior shoulder had been delivered that you knew you were home and dry. Well not exactly dry, but there was a great joy in giving the baby to the mother, then waiting for the placenta, hoping it would be trouble free, which in nearly all cases it was.

I loved to stand up thinking what a good job I had made of it. A typical male, of course. The mother had done all the hard work. If a midwife had been doing it, she would have made a better job of it, and if no one had been there, the mother would have managed on her own. I had read that in undeveloped countries, women would be literally labouring in a field. At the right time they would go to the edge of the field, have the baby, wrap it up then go back to work.

I had only read about it. I was delivering one baby when a consultant came in with some senior students; he was asking them various questions. I delivered the baby, and looked up to see that one of the students was Priscilla. As they moved on she said, 'Bob dear, can I book you as my midwife?'

'No,' I said, 'you are already delivered and I would have to put you back.'

She smiled, blew me a kiss and moved on with the rest. I could see two Hooray Henrys walking with her like two minders.

We were coming to the end of our midwifery and none of us had done a forceps delivery, although we had watched a few. There was a plastic pelvis and spine; inside was a life-size baby doll with its head down in the pelvis. The obstetric registrar was showing us how to do this instrument delivery. You had to slip your hand in so it was alongside the baby's head. Then you slipped the spoon-shaped small racket-like forceps blade up the inside of your hand so that it was covering one side of the baby's head. Then you did the same with the other blade, at the other side of the head. Then you clipped the handles of the two blades together, and gently pulled the head out of the pelvis. Some did it with a quick jerk; the reprimand being, 'You are not pulling a cork out of a bottle.' We all managed it to varying degrees. Jock, who had been hanging back, was the exception. With his huge hands, he just couldn't manage it. His hand got stuck in the pelvis with the blade jammed to the doll's head. In his struggles he pulled the whole lot onto the floor, slipping as he did so, and lay on the floor with the baby doll and the pelvis.

The registrar helped him up; picked up all the bits; handed the forceps to Jock and said, 'Now go and hit the father on the head with these and you will have killed the whole family.'

I was pretty certain that this was not original. My main memory of the midwifery was Priscilla's visit. I would have been happy to be her midwife providing I had been the baby's father. Some hope.

Being six months behind Priscilla was catastrophic. I virtually lost sight of her. I was always in a different situation to her. She was in the same clinical group as Joyda and I was continually asking him how she was. She was always warm and greeted me almost affectionately if we did bump into each other. 'Hello dear old Bob,' she would say. 'Where have you been hiding?' A brief word and then she was off; always with a trail of admirers behind her.

I had Christmas with my father and Louise; they always made a fuss of me. I had a card from Miles with a question, 'When are you coming to see me?', and a card from Priscilla from some Swiss skiing resort with the usual 'Compliments of the season'. I thought how well-mannered both Priscilla and her father were.

My clinical studies continued for the next two years. I was still playing too much rugby; Joyda had cut right back with his finals approaching, although I knew he would just walk it. As would, of course, Priscilla.

There was a great hush in the medical school at the end of spring, as all the people who I had started my training with sat their finals. Then a tense month while they waited for their results.

At last, one day there was pandemonium; as far as I could gather, virtually everybody of my intake had graduated, except me. I kept away from it. I was still just a student for at least six months. Of course, the top graduate in medicine in the whole of London was Joyda. He was his usual unassuming self. 'It's all a lot of rubbish,' he said. 'If I had been in Wales I would have been lucky to get in to the top ten.'

I was approached by the social secretary to run the bar at the Graduation Ball. I declined – I just could not have coped with it. I said, 'Alas, I will be away,' and I was going to make sure I was away.

I said to Joyda, 'Are you going to the Graduation Ball?'

'Good God no, who would ask me?'

'It's not about someone asking you, you have to ask some fair lady. What about Fat Nell?'

'Bugger off!' Fat Nell was sixteen stone and man-hungry. A couple of days later, there was a knock on my door. It was an agitated Joyda. 'I've been invited to the Ball.'

'Fat Nell?'

'Bugger off! I know you will never guess.'

'Then I won't try.'

'It was Priscilla.'

I don't know why, but I felt a flood of relief. Joyda was so fundamentally decent. 'What did you say?'

'I said to her, "I haven't got a dinner jacket". She said, "Hire one." It was more an ultimatum than an invitation. I think she just wants a Bob substitute.'

'Bollocks and double bollocks! I am not in her league.'

'Bob, I have no money and so many debts that I daren't try and borrow some more. What the hell should I do?'

'I will help you, don't forget we used to get a free ton of coal a month when I was mining,' I assured him, fishing my Post Office savings book from a drawer.

'I can't.'

'Okay, you go back to Priscilla and say you can't afford one. If you hadn't given up a summer to get me through second MB, I would not now still be at medical school.'

'Okay, I expect it's the lesser evil.'

'We'll go to Moss Bros together tomorrow and see if they can fit you out properly.'

'But, I don't dance.'

'Don't worry, Priscilla will teach you.' I didn't know how I knew, but I knew she would.

At Moss Bros they fitted Joyda out beautifully. He really looked smart and, in fact, rather fancied himself in it. I also gave him a paper bag with a gardenia in it.

'What's that for?' asked Joyda.

'It's a flower for Priscilla. This is what you give to your lady if you are taking her to a Ball.'

'Oh God! You bloody English, couldn't I just take a leek?'

'No. And promise me you won't say a word to Priscilla about the flower or the help with the dinner jacket.'

'I'll try not to.'

'Don't just "try not to" – don't,' I insisted.

I rang my father; I wanted to be out of the way. 'Could I come over?' I asked.

'Of course, are you free this weekend?'

'Yes.'

'Why not come for the whole weekend?' he said.

'I would love to,' I replied, relieved.

'What's troubling you, Bob?'

'Well, it's the Graduation Ball tonight and all the people I started out with will be moving on. I have at least six months before I get some sort of graduation.'

'Who's taking Priscilla to the Ball?' he asked.

'Why on earth did you ask about her?'

'You never talk about anyone else.'

'I don't believe that! She's actually going with Joyda.'

'I'm so pleased, we liked him immensely; he is a very bright boy. Tell me, did he ask her, or did she ask him?'

'Well, in fact, she asked him.'

'That figures, conversation over. Come as soon as you can and we'll take you out somewhere nice for dinner.'

'That will be absolutely splendid, Dad.' I hurried to get ready.

When I arrived, both Dad and Louise made a huge fuss of me. My father, who was usually very careful with money, really splashed out for me at a West End restaurant. When the wine arrived, they both raised their glasses to 'Dr Bob'.

'Dad, I am still a student.'

'Bob, it won't be long until you are one. We don't expect that you will become a professor of medicine, but we know that few doctors will be more loved or take better care of their patients.'

'How can you tell that?'

'Bob,' he said, 'there are some things that fathers know, that sons don't know. Now, what do you want to eat?'

The meal was superb.

I was given breakfast in bed on both the Saturday and Sunday, and for Sunday lunch we had some wine with the roast beef and Yorkshire pudding, followed by trifle.

I reluctantly made my way back to the medical school. It looked like a morgue. I went to my room. Nearly all the other rooms seemed to be empty. There was a light on in Joyda's room; I knocked at the door.

'Come in, Boyo, I've got a few cans in. I wanted to have a night with you before I set off. You've been a very good friend; I had thought of making you an honorary Welshman.'

'Bloody Hell – no! I think I would rather walk the

plank. Where are you off to?'

'Home for a month, then I am off to a hypertensive research unit in Glasgow.'

'Were you top of the list for London University?'

'I believe so. It's all a load of bollocks.'

'No, it isn't. You've also been a great friend of mine. Without you giving up a summer holiday, I wouldn't still be a medical student.'

'Bob, it would have been a terrible waste. I would like you as my GP if you ever live near me. Now, promise me something, if not a degree, certainly a diploma of some sort that will enable you to practice medicine. What I want you to promise is that if you don't get a degree in April and qualify with a diploma, that you'll finish your degree while you are doing House jobs.'

'Why?'

'Don't ask why. Just promise.'

'Okay, you're on. How did the Ball go?'

'I really enjoyed it. Priscilla, as well as being beautiful, is such a fundamentally nice person.'

'Were there a lot of Hooray Henrys queuing for her?'

'Yes, but I was her only partner for the whole evening and she patiently walked me round the dance floor. She and her father came knocking on your door this morning. I think they have left you a note. She is off to the neurology unit in Queen's Square.'

'You and I won't lose touch, will we Joyda?'

'Not a chance, Boyo. Now let's have another jar.'

We sat drinking and talking until midnight, when I went back to my room. There was a note that said, 'Please don't desert us, Bob. Miles and Priscilla x'

I thought, *How kind of them, but of course, that's what people like them do.*

CHAPTER FOUR

DR RAMSDEN AT LAST

I saw Joyda off in the morning. The place seemed to echo with emptiness, so I went out into town and had a coffee at Smokey Joe's, which was more smoky than Joe. I had a feeling that even the parrot could have smoked when no one was looking.

I got back to the medical school at lunchtime to find it heaving with children. Then I realised they were not children, they were all eighteen-year-old new medical students. In our cul-de-sac there were three grammar school boys and two Welsh boys from the same comprehensive school; both schoolboy rugby internationals almost certainly on scholarships. I thought, *good for them*. They started by calling me 'Sir' until I explained I was a final year medical student; then it was all questions, all at the same time. I said, 'Come on, I'll take you all for a cup of tea in the restaurant.'

They followed me in crocodile formation with all the lads taking things in. They were chirping round the table like a collection of parrots. I was holding forth about everything when Dai, the smallest of the Welsh boys, chirped up, 'Dad' and asked a question. Everybody laughed, but the name stuck. In the six months we were all together, I was always referred to as 'Dad' and there is no doubt that, in some ways, I acted as locum parentis.

I noticed that the two Welsh boys disappeared in the evenings for a couple of hours and used to come back pale and distraught. So I asked them both to pop in and see me. They came in looking sheepish. I said, 'What do you two get up to in the evenings?'

The chirpy one burst into tears. 'Dad,' he said, 'we are so homesick we just walk down to Paddington station to watch the Welsh trains come in hoping that we'll see somebody we know.'

'I know,' I sympathised. 'I was exactly the same when I started as a coal miner.'

'You were a coal miner, Dad?'

This was something they understood. They had been brought up among coal miners and coal mining and my having been a coal miner had some sort of reassuring effect on them. As far as I knew, they did not feel the need to trek to Paddington any more.

I, and what I called my 'kids', behaved very much like a family for the six months we shared the cul-de-sac. Most evenings, around 10.00 pm, we would gather round the little table near the electric cooker with a mug of cocoa or Ovaltine. During the day I really got my head down. I went to as many tutorials and lectures as I could and spent hours in the library.

These were not well-spent hours. I learned I took things in better if I was told or shown them, rather than reading about them. I had never been a great academic and sadly there was no Joyda to help me along. The more I tried to learn, the more I realised how little I knew, so I signed up to sit not just my degree – MBBS, but also as a back-up, the Society of Apothecaries – LMSSA, which is one of the City livery companies. It meant, if I wanted to, I was allowed to drive sheep through the centre of London or tie my horse to a lamppost. It was supposed to be easier than the degree, except for the midwifery, which was alleged to be harder. It would mean I was a doctor, and I knew of several who practised medicine with only this qualification.

The chief problem lay in getting a House job. If I passed my degree I would be able to pick almost any job at my teaching hospital, but only if I continued playing for the hospital rugby team. If I only got an LMSSA, I would have to scramble around to find some hospital that would take me. I would just have to stop being 'Good Old Bob' and do my best. This did not mean I could not have some quiet moments in my room thinking of Priscilla – wondering where she was, what she was doing and who she would be going out with. I had realised that she was out of my league, but it did not stop me thinking about her.

The time seemed to fly past and as I approached the exam date I realised, in spite of my efforts, how badly prepared I was. A week before my finals started I received a card from Priscilla and Miles with the message, 'Best of luck, Bob, just sock it to them.' I thought this was so sweet of them and felt it was the epitome of good breeding.

I had three solid weeks of examinations for the MBBS followed by the LMSSA at Apothecaries Hall, where you sat in a carpeted room with an open fire – quite gentlemanly. Apparently, in the past, you used to be given sherry at the start of each day. When I enquired, I was told that it had been stopped in 1890. With the MBBS I found the medicine part difficult. The surgery was okay; except in the oral examination, where there was a rather unpleasant surgeon who was short and a bit unkind with me. The midwifery also seemed fine; it was hands-on stuff, which I was best at.

Once I had finished, and after a couple of days with my father, I took my bicycle on a train to Glasgow and met up with Joyda. We had two weeks Youth Hosteling on the west coast of Scotland, which I found was incredibly beautiful. Joyda, of course, thought that it was quite good, but not as good as Wales. We cycled along the side of Loch Lomond. Joyda shouted, pointing to the far side of the loch, 'My God, there it is!'

'What?' I asked.

'The monster.'

'Which monster?' I asked.

'The Loch Ness monster. Is there another?'

'Yes. This is Loch Lomond. Loch Ness is about two hundred miles away.'

'Well, what is it?' asked Joyda.

'What is your long-range vision like?'

'Not too good. I'm awaiting glasses.'

'Get them soon. That is a man paddling a canoe. Don't you think it is beautiful here?'

'Well, it is large, but not as pretty as Lake Ogwen.'

'Bollocks! Lake Ogwen is just a pond.'

'How the hell do you know?'

'That was where my climbing career began and ended. A master at school offered to introduce three of us to climbing. I was all boy scout in those days. One of the three dropped out; his mother wouldn't let him go. We arrived at the bleak pond and it rained for the full five days. We stayed in a hostel and were to climb the Idwal Slabs. We set off in the rain the next day, roped up, and with the games master leading, me in the middle and Thomas the school scrum half coming up last. When I say climbing, this was hanging on to hairline cracks with your fingertips and struggling to find some degree of support for your feet. We seemed to be climbing up crevices. The games master went up first then I joined him, anchoring myself somehow in the crevice, and took in the loose rope as the scrum half shot up the rock like a monkey. The trouble was, being anchored in a crevice with rain pouring down, there was a small waterfall entering my trousers at the waist and more slowly leaving my trousers as, like all good climbers, I had my trousers tucked into my socks. This was all a nightmare. I thought, *somehow we have to get down all this lot.* After interminable hours, we reached the top. "How do we get down?" I asked. "Oh, we walk," said the games master and scrum half almost in unison. Looking down I could see gently sloping turf. I said, "Why didn't we walk up this way?" They said, "That would have taken away all the fun out of it." I thought, *my God, there must be something wrong with them or me.*

'There was no facility for drying our clothes and when we woke up it was literally pouring down; I did not fancy it. The games master was waiting for the weather report on the radio, then said, "I'm afraid there's no climbing for at least a couple of days." The scrum half threw his boots down in disgust. I spoke up. "Okay sir, we have to learn to take these thing on the chin." "Well done, Ramsden," he said, "I like your spirit." He drove us around for a couple of days then the weather cleared a bit. "We should be able to climb tomorrow." I had felt a sting in my left ankle during the day; a horse fly bite. That night it had swollen. I said to the games master, "I'm afraid I have a rather painful swollen ankle. I hope it is okay to climb." The games master replied, "No chance for you with an ankle like that. Your trouble, Ramsden, is that you have too much courage. I have seen it on the rugby field." So the two went off while I had two happy dry, warm days reading, making myself cups of tea and eating sandwiches. I sold my climbing boots as soon as I got home.'

While I had been telling my saga, Joyda had been killing himself with laughter. 'The trouble is,' he said, 'that the English are too bloody soft.'

I asked, 'How much climbing do you do?'

'I climb out of bed each morning. I'll settle for that.'

We pushed our bikes up the road which General Wade's troops had built after the Battle of Culloden. I pictured red-coated soldiers toiling with rocks and crow bars.

We crossed the Clyde Bridge, which was magnificent. We had a couple of days in Helensburgh, where we liked to sit with ice cream cones by the Clyde. In the evening, we'd go to the pictures, then back to the youth hostel. We turned round here and made our way slowly back to Glasgow. 'What a lovely country,' I said.

'Not as nice as Wales,' said Joyda.

'Bollocks!' I replied.

As soon as I got back from Glasgow I made my way to the Apothecaries Hall – no results yet. The next day I went just before lunch, looked at the Pass list and there was my name. Thank God, I had passed.

It was only when I walked away that I began to take in that I was actually now a doctor. I was both excited and apprehensive at the same time. The end of the long journey from Grammar School, coal mining, and now at the journey's end I wondered how I would cope having to take the full responsibility of medical situations.

I was shaken from my thoughts. 'Come on, Doctor, it's time to celebrate.' About half the rugby team was waiting for me. There had been a rumour that there was a good chance I might qualify. They carted me off to a pub, determined to get me drunk, and they were very successful. Not that it was difficult – I was not a great drinker. I never really liked draught beer and it didn't really like me. If asked what I would like to drink, I would say a sweet sherry, to everyone's dissent. This meant I had no choice. It was pint after pint of beer; I had no idea whether it was mild or bitter or a mixture. I was eventually both sick and unconscious; Big Jock had apparently carried me from a taxi to my room. I hadn't experienced a hangover before. I dreamed that the collier in the next stint was attacking my head with a pick. I woke up eventually to find all the kids sitting round my bed looking anxious.

'Are you ill, Dad?'

'I'm ashamed to say I was drunk for the first time last night.'

'We thought that might be it, Dad. But we have taken it in turns to sit by you. A man called Jock carried you in. He didn't look too well either. You were kissed as he carried you.'

'Not by Jock, for God's sake – he's not like that.'

'It was a very beautiful lady, she kissed you, on the forehead and said, "Dear Bob must have qualified. Thank you, Jock, for looking after him."'

'We told her, "He's our Dad – we'll look after him."'

'"Good," she said. "Is he a good dad?"'

'"Yes," we said. "The best."'

'Get out, before I burst into tears. I need sleep, and take this elephant that is sitting on my head with you!'

As they were leaving, I asked, 'Was this lady on her own?'

'No,' Dai answered, 'there were some Party Boys waiting in the corridor.'

'What's a Party Boy?'

'You know, a rich kid, who thinks they own the world.'

When they had gone I just groaned. Apart from feeling rubbish, there was the thought of Priscilla coming to see me and finding me drunk, with her entourage of Simpering Sams who would say, 'That's just what they would expect from an oik like him.'

I drank the kids' coffee, turned over and mercifully slept.

When I woke up I tried to ring my father and only got his secretary. I left a message, 'Dr Ramsden was trying to get in touch.'

When he called me back, he was delighted.

'I am only an Apothecary, as far as I know,' I said.

'That doesn't matter a bit; the best GP I ever had was an Apothecary. What about the degree?'

'I won't know for two weeks.' It was a huge boost to actually be a qualified doctor.

Two weeks later I went up to London University to find out my degree results. I scanned down the pass list. 'Bugger!' I hadn't passed. I then went to the detailed results. To my surprise, I had passed in Medicine and Midwifery, but just failed in Surgery. This wasn't too bad; exams were not my thing. I would have to find a House Surgeon surgical job, wherever; I just had this subject to clear off and I would have kept my promise to Joyda.

I scanned the *British Medical Journal* for jobs and found one for a House Surgeon at St Olive's Hospital in the East End, to start right away. I rang them and was told to come and see the consultant, a Mr Hines, the next day. I found out where it was, and I caught a bus out.

It was not an area that I knew. It became increasingly run-down the nearer I got to the hospital. When I arrived at St Olive's, I found it was in keeping with the surroundings; it would be difficult to find a hospital that looked more run-down than this one. I met Mr Hines, the surgeon; middle-aged and delightful.

'Bob,' he smiled, 'I love my work and I expect my staff to feel the same. Can you start tomorrow?'

Although I had planned to do something else I said,

'Of course, sir.'

'Great. I am almost run off my feet. I've had no Registrar or Houseman for three months. Now, tell me about yourself.'

I told him about my mining, and my rugby, and my desire to be a GP and that I had to finish off the surgery part of my MB.

'At the end of this job, you will fly through your examination. I think you and I will make a good team, but,' he said, 'let me warn you, after three months you will wish for a soft job, like working on the coalface with a pick and shovel. The area and the hospital look run-down but we are slowly trying to put the hospital right. There's a brand new maternity unit due to open here in six months' time and that will literally put new life into the hospital. This shabby area is the heart of London, if not the heart of Britain. You will find these East Enders the bravest and most polite patients you will ever meet. Although many houses are nearly falling down, all the front doorsteps are scrubbed every day and if you are ever invited into one, you will find it immaculate.

'But money is in very short supply for more substantial work. I like it here. I didn't play any games as a student; I just worked. I had to, my parents had used up every penny they had to get me through medical school. I won just about every prize there was, and could have had any House job I wanted at my teaching hospital, but in my day, not only weren't you paid, you also had to pay for your keep and laundry, and there was just no money left. So, I came here, where you did get free board and laundry.

'There are few better places to equip you for General Practice than here. You will see a bit of everything, particularly with midwifery, en route. I've been here all my working life – I love it. And, if you survive your job as my Houseman, I can see you spending a couple of years here. Particularly as you will need midwifery in General Practice.'

We shook hands. 'We'll see you tomorrow.'

A porter showed me to the room that was going to be mine, which like the rest of the hospital was run-down. He said, 'Here you are, you're one of the lucky ones, you have a gas ring. With the hospital food as it is, that will help.'

'How?' I asked.

'You'll have to wait and see,' he said.

I found later that only a few rooms had gas rings beside their gas fires, which meant you could cook and make hot drinks. Although the doctors' dining room seemed to be smart when I first saw it, the food turned out to be constantly appalling.

As I travelled back from the hospital, somehow the surrounding area that seemed so depressing on my way in, did not look so bad now. I did notice that all the houses had newly scrubbed steps.

When I got back I packed up all my stuff – clothes, books – then went shopping for basic supplies; tea, coffee, sugar, milk, bread, soup, baked beans, biscuits and eggs, and a small pan. I didn't buy any bacon as I couldn't see how I could cook it on my gas ring. I packed it all into a large cardboard box. I also went to the Post Office and made a big withdrawal.

The five kids had all been rushing about trying to help me; as a goodbye present they produced two tins of sardines. 'We're going to miss you, Dad,' they chorused as my taxi arrived. The emotional Dai had tears in his eyes.

'I am going to miss you lot. I think you are a great bunch and it's been a pleasure to have you as room-mates.' They helped me load up the taxi, then I was off.

Except for the examinations, I had thoroughly enjoyed

my student life. I still thought about Priscilla a lot. I couldn't see her fitting in to my East End life and I would have loved to have gone and seen her father, Sir Miles. I really liked him and to some extent I felt that the feeling was mutual. He had said, 'Look out for my daughter.' I now had to gear myself up to work harder than I ever had before.

CHAPTER FIVE

HOUSE JOBS

I arrived at the hospital, and started to unload the taxi when a hospital porter came up.

'Will give you a hand, Doc, which room are you in?'

He adorned himself with a massive amount of luggage to the extent I was able to carry the rest, and we did it all in one load. When I got to my room, the porter was putting the boxes down. 'What is your name?' I asked.

'Jack,' he replied.

I said, 'Thank you so much, Jack,' feeling in my pocket to give him a tip, when he said, 'None of that, Doc, we all look out for each other down here.'

'That's very generous of you.'

'That's the first time anyone called me that,' he said. 'I'll have to tell that to the missus!'

I unpacked as much as I could then went down to the doctors' dining room to find it was shut for the night. I came back to my room, made some toast on the gas fire, ate both tins of sardines the boys had given me, and finished with a cup of Ovaltine. After unpacking, I went to bed and set my alarm for 6.30 am.

When the alarm went off the next morning, I washed, shaved and did some more sorting out in my room, then went down to the doctors' dining room for breakfast. There was a nice Indian man called Henry who made me feel welcome, and three other uninterested doctors who just nodded. Henry gestured for me to sit next to him and said, 'If you enjoy badly cooked food you will enjoy this dining room. The cornflakes and toast are usually okay, but the rest is a lottery.'

'I will have a go at the scrambled egg.' I somehow managed to chew my way through it. We were joined by a very stout man who introduced himself as Hallum. Having seen what I had eaten he said, 'You will know the meaning of "egg bound" by the end of the day. I stick to fruit when it's available; if there isn't any, I buy some of my own.'

'I can always boil an egg on my gas ring,' I said.

'You are lucky to have a gas ring,' Henry replied.

'You are always welcome to come for a boiled egg and you can tell me about India. Where do you come from Hallum?'

'The Lebanon.'

'Between you, you can enrich me about both your countries,' I replied.

'Where are you working?'

'Mr Hines. He seems fine. I gather he has had no Registrar or House Surgeon for three months.'

They looked at each other and grinned. Then Hallum said, 'He is a brilliant surgeon, but forget about offering hospitality, you won't have time to sit down.'

'Well, please come and make your own use of the facilities if I'm not about. I gather from Jack the porter that we all look out for each other here.'

'Yes,' said Hallum, 'all the staff here are first class

except petty management jerks who are always on the prowl. And don't let Matron catch you drinking coffee on the wards – she hits the roof.'

I picked up my white coat, and made my way to the main surgical ward where I found Mr Hines, who had already started a ward round.

'Morning Bob. I usually start my round at 8.00 am, but you weren't to know.'

He then took me back to the patients he had seen and introduced me to them, not as his new House Surgeon, but as his colleague Dr Ramsden, who had come to join him. As he introduced me, he not only outlined the patient's medical condition, but would fill in social details like, 'This is Bill Lucas, he is captain of the local bowls team,' or 'George Price who has the grocery shop at the top of Queen Street.' There was no doubt his patients loved him, just as did the nurses and the ward sister.

When we had finished the round, he said, 'Bob, I know you are going to be run off your feet, but if possible try and find the time to make a social round each day. Just come and chat to the patients, not about their medical conditions, but their life in general; children, holidays, jobs, and a popular one is what happened to them during the war. The East End took a terrible pounding from air raids. It is just amazing some of the stories you will be told. Now come with me and scrub up, I need you to assist in a few operations. Hopefully you will be doing some of your own before the end of six months. There will be some new patients to clerk afterwards.'

He was a joy to assist; a brilliant surgeon, he made it all look so easy. He was calm and assured the whole time and he did not shout or throw things about, as I had seen some surgeons do at my teaching hospital. He did a gastrectomy and two hernias. He let me help him stitch up the hernia. He was a great man.

He told me to call him any time I was worried, and he never failed me. He painstakingly went through all the minor procedures with me; certain techniques for taking blood, best areas for putting up intravenous drips, lumbar punctures (taking fluid from the spinal cord) and plastering various broken bones.

As I gradually learned to do more of these things on my own, my feet barely hit the ground. What took up most of my time was examining and clerking new patients coming in. You started with a detailed history, including family history. The first young man I interviewed, a bus conductor called Gerald, when asked about his parents said, 'Both are dead.' When I enquired further, 'What did they die of?' his reply was, 'Nothing serious.' It wasn't always easy. In addition, as the hospital was short-staffed, I was often called to help out in Casualty and some of the other wards. But I really enjoyed my work.

It was only very occasionally that I could have fellow residents for late night chats. Henry and Hallum had free access to my gas ring and they and a few regulars used it most nights. Time seemed to fly by.

In my first two weeks I had a letter from Priscilla saying, 'How went the exams?' I made time to write at length to her, what the situation was and how busy I was.

She replied, 'Best of luck and I know, as always, that in addition to your own work "Good Old Bob" will be rushing round helping everybody. Your surgeon sounds first class. I am sure that he will shepherd you through your degree, but does it matter so much? My father joins me in congratulating you on becoming a Doctor, in his words, "rise from the ranks". He wishes you could be his doctor. I don't expect I would mind you being mine. I am not sure about neurology; I don't like the Senior Registrar, my bête noire as it were, and partly because a lot of it is so tedious – I am not working other than clerking, so it takes me hours just to clerk one patient. I have to do things like sensory perception in the mouth and map them, as well as everywhere else on the body.

'Thank goodness I have a holiday looming and a group of us are going off skiing in France. It's obviously no good asking you to join us. I hope that if you survive the next six months you will come and see us. My father is always going on about "When are you going to bring Bob, the coal miner, here to see me?" Until then, all good wishes, Priscilla.' I thought she could have said, 'Love, Priscilla.'

It started me off having daydreams about her – words from a song came back, about dreaming the impossible dream, which I realised this was. However, I could not remember any other words of the song, so I don't know how it finished.

They had to be daydreams, as I seemed to spend most of my nights rushing round the hospital and in the short bits of sleep I did get, as far as I could tell, she did not fit into any of my dreams. The professor I had heard at the Royal Institution said that you only remembered a dream if you woke up during it, or within five minutes of it ending. I did not do either of those, so perhaps it happened when I was flat out. I know sometimes at night the porters had to sprinkle cold water on my face to wake me up.

The longer I worked with Mr Hines, the more I admired him, and however busy we were he would put an hour aside each Friday for a surgical tutorial. He would sometimes set me areas of work, to be later questioned on. I felt as time went on that I was really getting to grips with the subject. Most days I managed to get what he called a 'social round' in; just going round getting to know patients and what they did in life. It probably meant that I got too close to them. I found I laughed and cried with them.

Unfortunately not all cases had happy endings. At one stage I did get a bit too big for my boots. A fit-looking man of about forty was admitted. He had been seen both at home and in outpatients without a concrete diagnosis. His GP had put him on six-hourly injections of morphine and every six hours he would be crying out for it. He was down for an exploratory diagnostic examination that afternoon. Mid-morning I was with the sister in her office when I heard him cry out for his morphia. Sister said, 'You could set your clock by his morphine shouts – it's practically to the minute.'

I had an inspired moment. I said, 'Sister, don't give him morphia, just give him an injection of distilled water.'

'Are you sure?' she asked.

'Yes, I take full responsibility.'

The sister gave him a distilled water injection and, just as with the morphine, he stopped shouting with pain and went off to sleep. 'That's incredible, Doctor,' she said. 'All the morphia we had pumped into that man!'

A couple of hours later, Mr Hines came to see the patients on his afternoon list. I was so pleased with myself, as I announced, 'Sir, I don't think you need to operate on Mr Laren,' and explained how clever I had been.

'Well, Bob. It's better to be safe than sorry.'

I thought, *What a waste of time and effort*. Mr Laren eventually came into theatre. Mr Hines opened him up and he was riddled with completely inoperable cancer. I felt so foolish. 'How do you explain the distilled water?' I asked.

'Bob, he had what is called a conditioned reflex. His mind knew that he'd had an injection, and it sent a message to his brain to say, "Your pain has been reduced" and so it was, and it's probable that you could do that a couple more times. Then his body would realise it was being conned. Throughout your medical life, you will come across this phenomenon in one way or another.'

We went to the sister's office for coffee after the list. I said to her, 'I feel such a fool.'

'And we thought we had a Boy Genius. But,' she said, 'I felt exactly the same as Dr Bob. We live and learn. I have put a scout out to warn us of Matron's whereabouts.'

'Now,' Mr Hines broke in, 'I have some news for you. I am off to New Zealand for three weeks next month, your last month here, Bob.'

Very sadly I asked, 'Will you be on call from New Zealand?'

'Of course. I have told this hospital that you can manage on your own. Now, what has made it possible is that a Senior Registrar is starting tomorrow; a delightful man called Alam Vetum Hussain. He is very experienced but will be pleased to have your help to settle in, Bob. I do hope that you will stay on here for a House Physician and Obstetrics job. The hospital will be sad to lose you.'

'Here, here!' said Sister. 'Good Old Dr Bob.'

'Do you know what I have told my new Registrar is the most important thing he has to do?' asked Mr Hines.

'No,' I replied.

'Well, it's your weekly surgical tutorial, and as soon as Sister has cleared the coffee cups, we will start this week's and I promise I won't talk about conditioned reflexes.'

'Do you address the new registrar as "Dr Alam Vetum Hussain"?'

'Unless you find an alternative version between you.

He has his FRCS, he uses "Mister" rather than "Doctor". I shall miss you Bob. You are the best House Surgeon I have ever had.'

I blushed. 'I feel so fortunate that I had you as my consultant, I had no idea that I have been here for nearly five months. If asked I would have said two days or ten years. I have lost track of time.'

Mr Hines declared, 'It's been a good blooding for you.' As he was saying this, a dark-skinned smiling man came through the door.

'Sir. You do have a long name,' I said.

'Just call me Sid,' was his reply.

'Sir Sid.'

'No,' he said laughing, 'just Sid. I came across a humorous English story a few weeks ago, where a man says "I don't mind what you call me, unless you call me late for breakfast". If I told that story in Baghdad no one would understand it. Its translation into Arabic is not easy.'

Mr Sid proved to be an excellent surgeon and an excellent doctor. He was, of course, not as accomplished as Mr Hines, but not too far off. Like Mr Hines, he said, 'Bob, you will see a bigger variety of conditions here than you would in a teaching hospital. I have just come from one, and ninety per cent of the patients on the medical ward are strokes.'

Somehow Sid trying to tell a humorous English story warmed me to him. Sid was a resident at the hospital, as I was. He insisted that he did three of the seven night duties each week and suddenly life became more manageable. I was actually sleeping whole nights on some nights. Strangely, it made me feel even more tired – until I got used to it.

Sid's tutorials were even more challenging than Mr Hines's. At last my surgery exam arrived and I went full of confidence, which is perhaps not the wisest approach.

I found the surgical papers fairly straightforward and was as careful as possible answering the questions. Then two days later, I had the oral exam (viva). I had the same surgeon as last time. Help! He looked at my file, at the marks for the papers, and then stared at me, saying, 'I have really got to test you.'

Fortunately I had answers to all his questions. When we finished the viva he actually smiled. 'Are you going to sit your FRCS?' he said. 'I am not supposed to tell you this, but you got through with a Distinction. What are you going to do?'

'I'm going to be a GP.'

'That's a bit of a waste; you have obviously been doing a surgical House job. Who did you work for?'

'Mr Hines.'

'I understand we call him the "Star in the East". He was a contemporary of mine at medical school. I don't know why he did not take a House job there.'

'He is happy where he is.'

When I got back to St Olive's, Sid was waiting for me. 'How did it go?'

'I have a Distinction. I have my degree now,' I said.

'How do you know? The results won't be out.'

'They told me off the record.'

'I'm not surprised.'

'The oral examiner said I should go on to be a surgeon.'

'You would make a very good one,' said Sid, 'but you are purpose-built for General Practice. Are you going to have a shot at going back to your teaching hospital?'

'No. I am going to have a shot at the House Physician's job here, then if that goes alright I will have a try for one of the two Senior House jobs in obstetrics.'

'Well, you have the House job here, if you want it. I spoke to Dr Jackson the consultant and asked him what would happen if you applied for his House job. He said he would take you like a shot. Now come back to my room for a glass of mint tea.'

'You mean that in one day I have a hypothetical medical degree and a House Physician's job?'

'It's all true. That's how the cookie crumbles, or is it how the crumbles cookie?'

'It's something like that,' I said. 'Now for the mint tea, it's a new drink for me.'

'Well,' said Sid, 'it's a bit like British Yorkshire Pudding, once you have had three glasses of it your hunger is assuaged.'

'Why three glasses? I might not like it.'

'Don't try and chicken, or duck, or turkey, out of it. The three glasses; the first is for Allah, the second is for all the people in the world and the third is for ourselves.'

'Sid have you ever thought of being a stand-up comedian?'

'Perhaps just a bumbling sitting one,' he replied.

I was interviewed by the medical consultant Dr Jackson and his Registrar, Dr Shariff, the next week. He seemed fairly remote but pleasant, and I already knew the registrar from the medical staff dining room. He was nice enough, but did not compare to Sid. They confirmed that they wanted me to start in two weeks, so I had time to journey up to Glasgow to have a week with Joyda.

Joyda was a good solid friend. He greeted me with, 'Well done, Bob.'

'Joyda, I did not dare to fail with your shadow looming over me.' Then I said, 'Joyda, if I would ever marry, would you be my best man?'

'Would Priscilla mind?'

'What has it to do with her? I have as much chance of marrying Priscilla as I have of climbing Mount Everest, or being Prime Minister.'

'All three are possible,' said Joyda. 'Now have a look at my Welsh beauty.' He whipped out a photograph of the most beautiful Welsh girl.

'Is she Miss World?'

'No, that is my Irene. We are to be engaged next month and get married in a year's time. I can't ask you to be my Best Man, I have to ask my brother, but I do hope you will be one of my ushers.'

'Of course,' I said, and for the first time that I remember, I felt jealous of Joyda. How I would have loved *The Impossible*, if I could have said it about Priscilla and myself.

'Come on,' Joyda smiled, 'we have something to celebrate. I have booked a meal for us at the best hotel in Glasgow. I am so pleased for you, Bob.'

'Joyda, I am so pleased for you too, Irene looks delightful; where did you meet her?'

'At school,' he said. 'I had to fight off a lot of competition.'

'You have never mentioned her before.'

'Do you think I was going to risk her amongst buggers like you in London? No, we have loved each other for many years, but kept it between us. We Welsh are different you know.'

'I know, you worship rugby and leeks!'

'Perhaps it's enough. Give me your case and then let's go off to eat.'

We wined and dined for the whole week. Went to a few cinemas and a theatre; quite different to our last holiday. 'Wining and dining', except for the first night, was a bit of an exaggeration as most places we ate in were unlicensed and often the main course would be egg and chips or Welsh Rarebit with the occasional splash out on a Buck Rarebit.

We went to two art galleries; not that either of us were artistically inclined or really interested. We did appreciate, and see, some beautiful paintings. We were never sure by whom unless there was a clear label. We only did it because we thought that was the sort of thing you are supposed to do; handy material for making small talk.

CHAPTER SIX

REUNION

I came to my HP job a bit Gung Ho! with the distinction in surgery behind me. I had never had a distinction in anything before except, of course, rugby. But that was different. There was also a difference in the surgical team and the medical one. Dr Jackson never ever called me Bob, it was always Dr Ramsden. Dr Sharrif always called me Bob, but I never had any idea of his first name and he never gave details of his home life or background. He was a very private person and quite shy, but fundamentally a decent man who was studying to pass his membership. I think that he was very religious as he was always popping off for a few moments. I believe it was to say his prayers. I thought that he was from Saudi Arabia or Iran. The fact that he and Sid, who was from Iraq, politely had nothing to do with each other meant it was more likely to be Iran. This did not stop him from being a pleasure for me to work with. He was patient in his instruction and teaching.

On a ward round, we stopped by a patient who had had a coronary. He handed me an ECG result, which in those days were on plastic film. 'What do you make of that?'

Having no idea, I said, 'I am not sure.'

He smiled. 'It does help, Bob, if you don't hold it upside down.'

As time went on I did become familiar with such things as elevated T waves and long PR intervals, but I never really enjoyed the technical side of medicine.

One of my most vivid memories of my HP job was having to give mouth to mouth resuscitation to a single toothed tramp. If it had been the Olympics, he would have got a gold medal in halitosis.

Thinking I knew it all, after my surgical triumph, my House Physician job was a continual learning process. We had admitted an unconscious man with a high fever and stiff neck. A fairly obvious acute meningitis. I did a lumbar puncture and took out some cloudy fluid and sent it off to the lab to culture the offending bacteria and find out what it was sensitive to. In the interim, as the procedure would take two to three days, Drs Jackson and Sharrif prescribed a basket of antibiotics to be given until the offending bacteria was cultured and sensitivity assessed. Happily, the patient recovered rapidly and within twenty-four hours had regained consciousness and was taking fluids by mouth as well as by drip. We were all congratulating ourselves when the culture result of the spinal fluid came through that showed a bacteria that was resistant to the antibiotics we were giving the patient, but sensitive to other antibiotics. We immediately changed to what we thought would be the right antibiotics only to have the patient's health plummet, and he drifted back into unconsciousness. So we switched back to the first lot of antibiotics and he responded again, and after a further ten days had made a complete recovery. On the last ward round, before the patient was discharged, Dr Jackson said, 'Now what do you make of this, young man (the patient was about forty years old), Dr Ramsden?'

I said, 'I am a bit confused, sir. I thought the bacteria cultured would be the cause of the trouble.'

'Nine times out of ten it is. But there is always the exception to the rule. The answer is constant vigilance.' Turning to the patient, he continued, 'You can go home tomorrow, you have been treated and investigated by the best lumbar puncturist in the hospital,' indicating me. I blushed.

The patient said, 'I don't know what all that means, but thank you, Dr Ramsden.'

I blushed again. It fulfilled that idiom that in medicine you get credit when you don't deserve it and discredit when you don't deserve it, but above all, you get more credit than you deserve.

The downside to medical wards as opposed to surgical ones is that you get many more long term patients than you do in surgery – patients with strokes, heart and lung conditions. You got the odd cardiac arrest but generally everything was at a slower pace. I did have more time to do my social rounds as outlined by Mr Hines and got to know my patients and their families almost too well, as some of them died and I got caught up in the family grief. It was a rewarding six months.

At the end of my six months, Dr Jackson gave me a bottle of whisky and said, 'Well done, Ramsden, I think you will make a good GP.' and Dr Sharrif said, 'It's been a pleasure working with you, Bob. When I pass my membership I will go back to Iran (I was right) as a consultant. Here is our family address; if you should ever come to Iran, please come and see us. Also,' he said, 'I do hope that you win the hand of the lady you are always talking about.'

'Which lady am I always talking about?'

He said, 'Priscilla. She sounds lovely. Does she realise that St Olive's leading lumbar puncturist is her devoted admirer?'

'I do apologise,' I said. 'Unfortunately I am not in her league.'

'Bob,' he said, 'we are all in the same league in the sight of Allah, don't forget.'

Dr Sharrif was a very decent man. I could never get him to come to our Groupie meetings. I said, 'Best of luck with your membership, Dr Sharrif.'

He replied, 'I think it will be alright.' And knowing him, I knew it would be.

I was interviewed and accepted for a Senior House Officer job in the new gynaecological and midwifery unit. When asked if I was hoping to sit my DRCOG (Diploma in Obstetrics and Gynaecology)?' I said, 'Yes.' Having passed my MB surgery with a Distinction, examinations did not seem too formidable. It would mean extra weekly lectures that were the equivalent of Mr Hines's tutorials.

I had virtually no social life. I never took a nurse out. A Swedish girl did hint that she was up for most things, if I was interested. I thought, *why not?* Then a picture of Priscilla seemed to float through the back of my eyes and I thought, *how could I be unfaithful?* Which was silly really as I most likely would never meet her again.

I could not believe the same thoughts might be passing through her mind. I knew that I had an open invitation to visit her and Sir Miles at Boyston Hall. I found that open invitations on the whole did not work, especially in my later years in medicine, and particularly in bereavement. If you say to the bereaved, 'You can pop in and see us at any time,' they do not come, even if you mean it. I'm sure there are exceptions; I found mainly you had to give time and date specifically, and for the bereaved, weekends were the worst and most invitations to Sunday lunch were gratefully accepted.

There were a few parties in the doctors' mess, but I went to my room, most often sitting there with a soft drink. I went to watch a few rugby games and met up with some old friends, who all seemed to be getting married. And from time to time I went to my father's for the weekend, making sure I did not go too often.

For some reason my room became a sort of meeting room. Most evenings, when I was there, people would drift in; I seemed to collect lost souls who came from other countries, such as Jamaica, a girl from Nigeria, the lovely looking Swedish girl, a not too good looking Brazilian girl; with Henry, Hallum and Sid as the most consistent regulars.

I started my SHO job in obstetrics and gynaecology. It meant a boost in salary and was hands-on stuff, which I was much better at. There was also a lady SHO and excellent midwives, so I had reasonable time off which was great. Being a SHO meant you had to sign up for a year. I had the feeling that Marie Stopes, the contraception authority, had never visited this part of London, as many mothers were having their eighth or ninth baby and delivery was more like taking a pass from a rugby scrum than an actual slow delivery. It was a very cheerful and a very good and well-equipped unit.

I had been doing the job for three months when the hospital secretary came into the mess one lunchtime and announced that what was called 'The West End Neurological Unit' would be coming to the hospital for six months. They would not be resident but would share the dining room at lunchtime. There was a shout of 'Lucky them!' from almost everyone.

I thought nothing more of it until a couple of weeks later. I went in late for lunch. There was only one person still left; a girl getting up from the table. 'Oh God! It's

Priscilla!' Without thinking, I went straight to her, gave her a hug and said, 'How lovely to see you.'

She said, 'The same here, Bob. I didn't realise you would still be here.' We were still touching. I would not have dared to do this if I had thought about it. We were just looking at each other when we were interrupted by a voice saying, 'Priscilla, stop smooching with another of your admirers and get off and clerk those patients.'

I had heard of a red mist coming over people's eyes. For the first time, it did with me. An almost uncontrollable rage came over me; I left Priscilla and walked over to this man who was about my height and weight. I stood menacingly in front of him, my face about six inches from his. I said, 'Who do you think you are?'

'I am the Senior Neurological Registrar and Priscilla is my SHO.'

'That's funny. When I shook my shirt tail this morning something bigger than you fell out.'

'That's disgusting!'

He was getting a bit flustered; he could see that I wanted to smash his head against the wall, which thank God I didn't. It was a close call. I said, 'I find you disgusting too. Priscilla and her father are very old friends of mine and I have not seen her for a very long time. You will apologise to her and, if you are rude to her, or me, again, being the Senior Resident here I will speak to the catering committee and get you banned from this dining room. Now apologise and get out!'

He muttered, 'I beg your pardon, Priscilla,' and he shot off.

'Bob,' said Priscilla, 'I have never seen this side of you before.'

'I did not know I had this side of me,' I replied. 'The worrying thing was I wanted to kill him.'

'I think that's what he thought. Good for you, he is a

creep and always wanting to take me out and I won't go. But, how you have risen in the world, Senior Resident and a major influence on the catering committee!'

'I'm not the Senior Resident and I don't think there is a catering committee.'

'Bob, you are such a scream. I think you frightened him to death.'

'I do apologise. I've not been like that before. Do let me know if he gives you any more trouble.'

'I daren't. I don't want blood on my hands! My father is always asking after you. I must go back to work; we are so busy. We have this project to complete in six months; it is rare for me to get to lunch and we have to get back to Queen's Square in the evening. Thank you, my knight in shining armour, we are bound to bump into each other over the next five months. I am sorry that I can't be quite certain and fix a time; you know how it is. But, it is really good to see you again.' She gave me a peck on the cheek, and then she was gone.

I found it all difficult to take in. By sheer chance, Priscilla had landed on my doorstep. Her arrival coincided with my fellow SHO going off sick, so my work had almost doubled. In addition, every area that I had helped out in seemed to want me at once. That included surgical wards, medical wards and Casualty. I tried to get into lunch as often as possible.

The West End Unit used to arrive by coach at 10.00 am each day, then left by the same coach at 4.30 pm. I tried to hang about and get a glimpse of her. Twice I had a wave from the bus window. Twice she was at lunch surrounded as usual by Hooray Henrys, but neurological ones. Then it was very rare to see any of them at all at lunch. Henry said he had spotted them having packed lunches in an empty ward. Was this because the food was so terrible, or had I frightened their chief man off? Sometimes a few of them would come over for a post-lunch coffee. No sign of Priscilla, not even a hint that she had tried to get in touch with me.

A welcome diversion; a note from my father. He and Louise would be away the following Friday and he enclosed two tickets for the Royal Institution. The subject was the Van Eyk polyptych of the Holy Lamb of Ghent. I had two tickets and I did not want to go on my own. I was at a loss to know who to ask. I wandered down to the hospital dining room and there was Priscilla, on her own.

Oh God, I thought, *dare I go and ask her?* I found I was walking towards her whilst I was still thinking of what I was going to say. I went up to the other side of her table. She looked up.

'Bob, how nice to see you! I thought you had disappeared forever.'

I now started to get tongue-tied and didn't seem to be able to get out a coherent sentence.

'Bob, are you trying to ask me something?'

'Yes, but it sounds so foolish. You will think I am nuts.'

'Try me.'

'Would you like to come with me on Friday to hear a talk about the Van Eyk polyptych of the Holy Lamb of Ghent at the Royal Institution?'

Her face lit up. 'I would just love to.'

'There is one drawback, I have to wear a dinner jacket and you would have to wear an evening dress.'

'Bob, that makes it even better still. Oh Bob, how absolutely lovely. I will be going out with a real person to something real, instead of being dragged off to various nightclubs. I had almost given up on people.'

'I do hope you will forgive me if I am clumsy, you are the first girl I have ever taken out.'

She looked puzzled. 'Bob, have you never had a date?'

'Yes,' I said. 'I had one once when I was coal mining.'

'What happened?' she asked.

'She didn't turn up.'

Priscilla said, 'Too often I could weep for you.' She bit her lip and tears seemed to come into her eyes. 'The stupid girl. Bob, you so underestimate yourself. My father thinks you are special.'

'I think that he is the finest of gentlemen and still weeps for the young men of Arnhem, particularly the young miners.'

'You are absolutely right about my father, that is the part of him that is the dearest; I love him to bits. He will be pleased to hear I am going out with you and don't ask me to explain. I am so excited about Friday. It has given me a sort of "kiss of life".'

'I would always be happy to give you the *kiss of life*.'

'No you wouldn't,' she said. 'Not in front of your Rugby Buggah friends.'

'Is that was people call us?'

'No, that's what I call you; all you do is chase a ball around a field. It's just not that important, is it?'

'I see.'

'Bob, don't be so agreeable, of course it's important, but not the be all and end all. I will not let you down and I shall look my best for you.'

'Oh God. I will do my best too. I can't be called a snappy dresser.'

She asked, 'Do we get Hunter?'

'No, he is the property of the Central Electricity Generating Board.'

'Does he always call you "Master Robert"?'

'No, he was taking the piss; I mean the mickey. I was very rude to him.'

'Oh. I am sorry to hear that. What did he say back?'

'He said "Bollocks!" and then I said something else to

him and his reply was "The only thing I can think of is to repeat "Bollocks!".'

'He sounds my sort of man! Will I know what you said to him?'

'No.'

'If you like, I could get my father to send a car.'

'No, we will get a taxi. I am taking you out.'

'Can we split the expense?'

'No, don't forget, you are my first date who is actually going to turn up.'

'Bob dear, I must fly. You have no idea how much I am looking forward to it.'

'Yes, I do,' I said. 'It will be about half as much as I am looking forward to it.'

She blew a kiss, then she was gone. I somehow got back to my room and lay down on my bed. I was completely smashed. I walked round in a sort of daze for the rest of the week. I got my dinner jacket checked and bought a flower for Priscilla. I almost jumped out of my boots when he told me how much it was.

'God,' I said, 'is that how much it costs?'

'Yes,' replied the florist. 'What did you expect to pay for one of those?'

'I had no idea.'

'Well you know now.'

I had looked at my Post Office savings book where I had squirrelled away money when I was mining. It was much healthier than I had thought. I booked a taxi for 7.00 pm and a table at a small inexpensive restaurant for 10.30 pm; one which my father and I sometime went to after the Friday night discussions.

Come the Friday, I was at the hospital entrance, dinner jacket on, flower in a paper bag. Priscilla arrived, driven by her brother, at about ten to seven.

Mark, her brother, came in to say hello. He seemed a really nice young man. 'Hello, Bob,' he said. 'I hear that you once won the rugby cup on your own.'

I nodded towards Priscilla. 'I was inspired.'

'I don't believe it,' he replied. 'She has never inspired me to do anything. Now, can I give you both a lift to the Royal Institution?'

'Thanks so much. I have a taxi coming at 7.00 pm.'

'Fine. Will look forward to seeing you again.' And then he went.

'What a nice young man,' I said to Priscilla.

'He obviously likes you.'

'Your family seem to like very quickly.'

'We do. You are a very nice person.' Then she added, 'You look very smart in a dinner jacket.'

'It's my father's old one.'

She almost groaned. 'Bob, you don't have to tell me that. I don't care if your great grandfather wore it in the Crimea. Please do not be so humble; you look really smart.'

I said, 'And you look exquisite.'

'Heavens, that is the first time anybody called me exquisite.'

'There is always a first time for everything.'

We got into the taxi, and I handed her the paper bag. 'I have a flower for you.'

'How sweet of you,' she exclaimed. 'Oh my God, it's an orchid! It is the first one I have ever had.' She seemed to sort of choke for a moment. Then she said, 'Bob there is something about you that always makes me want to cry. You must have done without food to buy this.'

'Who wants food? Don't forget we got a free ton of coal a month when we were mining. Please don't cry.'

'No' she said, 'it's difficult not to.'

We arrived at the Royal Institution and handed in our coats, then promenaded around the gallery looking at the window casements of the scientists who had worked there. We stopped at Faraday's window display then moved on to Humphrey Davy.

'I know why we are lingering here,' said Priscilla. 'Davy's miner's safety lamp.'

'You're right.'

She asked, 'Would you have liked to carry on as a coal miner?'

'Definitely not. They were a great lot, it was a privilege to be with them and it was a great experience, but two-and-a-half years was plenty.'

As we walked around the gallery, she had slipped her hand in my arm. I had never felt happier – it seemed as if she read my thoughts as almost simultaneously she said, 'I am just loving this. Do you know much about polyptyches, Bob?'

'I don't even know what they are, but lectures here are aimed at people like me. They are introducing you gently into something you may not know about.'

'That suits me. I know that a "polyptych" is a sort of religious painting. This one is special; you see a tiny window and if you look through it, you can see the whole of a street scene. It's quite incredible. You can see people, horses and carriages. I would love to go over and see it one day.'

We went down and had coffee and canapés amongst a lot of dinner-jacketed men and beautiful elegant women. Not one was nearly as beautiful or elegant as Priscilla. I was so proud of her. We found our seats in the auditorium and at 9.00 pm a bell pinged and the lecturer gave a fascinating talk, expanding on what Priscilla had told me. It was so interesting. I have enjoyed few talks more. I was wanting more, when with perfect timing, as the lecturer was saying his last sentence, the 10.00 pm bell rang and he walked out.

'That was tremendous,' said Priscilla. 'And Bob, my father said if we would like to be his guests for supper, there is a table for two at his Club.'

'Please thank him so much but tonight it is my night and I have already booked us a table at a humble restaurant. There is even a half-bottle of Mateus Rosé being chilled for us. It is the only wine I know.'

'That's what my father said you would say.'

'I do hope I have not offended him.'

'No, you will have pleased him that his prediction was right.'

It was only a short walk to the little restaurant I had booked. 'I do hope Mateus Rosé is okay for you,' I said.

'Bob, it will be fine and in keeping with the tradition, I will take the bottle home and make a table lamp of it.'

I said, 'It's only a half-bottle.'

She laughed. 'It will just be a small lamp – for my boudoir.'

The meal passed too quickly. We did not bother too much about what we were eating; we were just engaged in talking. Eventually there were signs that they wanted to close the restaurant. 'Priscilla,' I said, 'I will order a taxi and take you home.'

'It's going to cost the earth. Can we split the fare?'

'No, don't forget we got a free ton of coal a month when I was mining.'

'Are you going to pay him in coal?'

'No, I might give him a tip.'

'Touché!' she said.

We were strangely silent in the taxi. We eventually reached the gates of Boyston Hall. 'Would you like to come in?' she asked.

'That is very sweet of you, but I ought to be getting back.'

We stood rather solemnly outside the taxi and she said, 'Bob, from tomorrow I go away for three weeks. In four weeks we are celebrating my twenty-fifth birthday here. You will receive an invitation. Please come.'

'Of course I will come, if I can.'

She stood quietly and said, 'This has been a very special evening for me.'

'Me too,' I replied.

Then she gently touched the side of my face. 'Bob dear, you have to decide if you want to spend the rest of your life being "good old reliable Bob" or if you want to get out and about as we did tonight.'

'I hadn't thought of things like that.'

She said, 'Please start thinking now. I don't remember ever having a better evening. Thank you.' She slipped through the gates and was gone.

The taxi drove back to the hospital as I mulled over what she had said. When I arrived at the hospital, it was surrounded by more ambulances and police cars than I had ever seen before. The cause was a crash between two coaches. Casualty was just heaving with all sorts of people with all sorts of injuries; I had never ever seen such a mass of people in Casualty before. I saw the whole of our group were hard at it, so I took off my dinner jacket, hung it in the sister's office and got stuck in. 'Good old Bob,' several said, 'it's nice to have a bit of class in Casualty.'

The term 'Good old Bob' seemed to be going to haunt me. We all just about worked through the whole night – there would be no Groupie meeting tonight. Apart from work, my mind was just full of Priscilla. I had to keep reminding myself she was not available for the likes of me.

The invitation to her twenty-fifth came at last. 'Sir Miles Justin Boyston, et cetera, et cetera, requests the pleasure of inviting Dr Bob Ramsden to his daughter's twenty-fifth birthday on 21st August.'

Then a programme: 11.00 am point-to-point races at some place I had never heard of, followed by polo at the Hurlingham Club where a dinner and dance would follow in the evening. Then it said, 'dress informal.'

What did that mean? I assumed it meant not dinner jackets, so I quickly had my only suit cleaned. Then, I thought, *a present with all those rich kids to compete with*. I went to look at a jewellers and was struck straight away by a massive moonstone pendant. I enquired the price. £495. God Almighty! I could not afford that, but somehow I was going to get it. My father had always said he kept a slush fund for me, which I had never approached him for. So I rang him. 'Dad, is there any chance that my slush fund could come up with £500?'

'Yes,' said my father. 'You never approached me before.'

'I will pay you back.'

'No you won't. I gather it must be very important.'

'Yes, it is, for me.'

'Well I won't ask any questions. There is more if you require it.'

'No,' I said, 'that's just fine.'

I paid his cheque into the bank as soon as it arrived; waited until it cleared, rushed to the jewellers and, thank God, it was still there. I thought it was beautiful and bought it. As the birthday approached I was filled with apprehension.

The great day arrived. I caught the train, then a taxi, arriving at about 10.30 am and, my God, I was the only one in a suit. Many were in open-necked shirts and, of course, blazers and jodhpurs. *They must be the polo players*. In a minute Priscilla had rushed up. 'Bob, I am so pleased you made it.' She kissed me on the cheek. 'Don't take any notice of all this lot. They are just clutter.'

I gave her the present.

'Thank you so much. I will look forward to seeing what it is. Knowing you, you will have broken the bank for whatever it is.'

'No,' I said, lying, 'it's just a little something.'

All the time we were talking, people were trying to drag her away. 'Come on Prissy! We'll miss the first race.'

'Are you coming along?' asked Priscilla.

'No, he's not,' said her father, who had come up from behind. 'I want him.'

'Hope to see you later,' said Priscilla rather wistfully, and went off with the crowd I certainly did not belong to.

'I don't think you wanted to go to the point-to-point,' said Miles.

I said, 'You are a mind reader.'

'Come with me,' he said, 'I want to hear all about coal mining, then I will show you round this place I am the guardian of. Would you like a little lunch with me here?'

'I would love it, sir.'

'Sir,' he said. 'My name's Miles.'

'It's not a title "Sir",' I explained, 'it's just respect for a more mature man.'

'Okay. I will accept that. Now about coal mining.'

As I started to explain I found that I was having a sort of friendly court martial. He wanted to know every detail: What was a stint? How much coal did that mean? Where did I live and how much was I paid? How thick was the coal seam? And he went on to refer to the much narrower seams in Durham. He seemed to be quite well-acquainted with coal miners and coal mining. I remember him talking about the miners in his platoon at Arnhem the day we first met. I could just see him chatting with his lads, who, he said, when it came to the battle, were the steadiest of the lot. But they were all killed, so I did not bring the subject up.

When we had exhausted coal mining he said, 'I think you did a great job, Bob. You had a tougher time than many soldiers.'

I replied, 'I was in a safe civilian job and no one was trying to kill us and there were 750,000 men doing the same job.'

'Now for lunch.'

We had a ham salad and a glass of white wine. He said, 'Bob, I do wish Priscilla would not surround herself with all that clutter.'

I said, 'She probably doesn't. She stands out like a beacon that they all rush towards.'

'Perhaps you are right, Bob. I hadn't thought of it that way. You are a wise old head on a young man.'

'I just wish I were.'

'Do you like Priscilla?'

'Yes, I think she is the nicest person I have ever met. In a way, I am part of the clutter.'

'No you're not.' He asked again, 'Do you really like her?'

I said, 'That's a word I could not use to describe her. I think she is the nicest, most beautiful person I have ever seen or met.'

'I am pleased to hear that,' he said. 'Now for the grand tour.' He took me round every room of his lovely house. Portraits of relatives going back hundreds of years.

'You must be very proud of them.'

'No, they were a rotten lot of thieves and pirates. Inwardly I'm ashamed of them all,' he said. 'I just have this house and all it contains – it's not big enough to open to the public, thank God. I would hate that. I don't know how long we are going to be able to afford it all. My son Mark is taking care of things.'

'He seems a very nice young man.'

Having explored just about everywhere, he said 'I will now take you to my special room.' As we were going there he asked, 'Have you any family history, Bob?'

'Yes. I am the first doctor, as far as I am able to tell.

There were generations of pipe laggers – whatever that means. One man was obviously educated as he managed someone's estate.'

'Here we are,' he said and opened a heavy locked door. Inside the room was a window looking over roaming hills going off into the distance. The walls were covered in black and white sketches. Some were signed by quite famous artists, most of them by Miles himself. They were great, and I said so. 'Is this your thing?'

'Yes, very much so.'

I looked through them all carefully, especially the ones by friends at the Sketch Club, and to my great surprise I recognised one of me. I said, 'Sir, there is one of me.'

'Where?' he said. 'This is by my friend Andrew Ramsden.'

'Yes. I am Bob Ramsden, his son.'

He said, 'I thought that your father still worked down the coal mines.'

'No,' I said, 'he was the colliery electrical engineer at Silverwood Colliery, where I was born. He has become a very well-known electrical engineer.'

'I know,' Sir Miles said. 'Isn't he in charge of producing all our electricity? And is his lovely wife Louise your mother?'

'No. Step-mother.'

'So,' said Sir Miles, 'when did your family stop being pipe laggers?'

'I have my grandfather's diaries from 1902 to 1915. His New Year Resolution, in 1902, was to get out of the pit where he worked as a collier for thirty shillings a week. In 1934 he took his wife and youngest son on a world cruise. My father left grammar school at fifteen; he was a late developer and has prospered. I shall never be as bright as him. I am a not a very bright plodder.

'My grandfather's sister went to New Zealand where

they had a small grocer's shop. Her son, my Uncle Charlie, won a scholarship to RAF Cranwell, and on the same Honours List that Uncle Charlie was knighted as a Marshall of the Royal Air Force, my father got a CBE. How proud my grandfather would have been.'

'That is a lovely story, Bob. Overall your family shows up better than ours.'

'I would not say that, sir, none of them were at Arnhem.'

'Okay,' he said, 'I don't talk about that.'

'I know, sir,' I replied, 'and I will remember not to bring it up again.'

'A cup of tea, Bob?'

'Yes please, sir.'

We went off to the large kitchen and made it between us. We seemed like old friends. 'Bob,' he said, 'I have the feeling that you are not wanting to dance at Hurlingham.'

'You are right, sir. I hope that I am not letting Priscilla down.'

'No, but she will miss you.'

'Sir, as soon as I try to speak to her, someone pulls her away. If I may sir, I will ring for a taxi and slip back to the hospital.'

'No,' he said, 'it will be my pleasure to take you back.'

In spite of my protests he did and we chatted amicably on the way back. When we got to the hospital he said, 'This looks a bit of a dump.'

'It is not as bad as it looks, and it is improving. In fact, it's difficult to explain. This is a good area and a good place to work in.'

He asked, 'Didn't you have an exam to clear up?'

'Yes,' I said. 'I was only an Apothecary. I finished my degree happily without a problem. But, I am exactly the same sort of doctor as I was before; it just means people don't look down on you. It's all a bit sad.'

'Bob,' Sir Miles said, 'you never mention your mother.'

'No. She and my father grew up at different rates and she went off with some chap and they were both killed in a car accident when I was young. She seemed a nice enough lady but I never really got to know her. Happily my father and I are very close.'

'Good. My wife died a horrible death from cancer six years ago; somehow each day the loss does not reduce.'

'I am so sorry, sir.'

'Do try and find a cure for it.'

'I will do my best, sir.'

'Bob,' he said, as he was about to drive away, 'whatever, you are always welcome in my house.'

'Thank you, sir,' I replied. 'I have really enjoyed my day and will look forward to seeing you again.'

Having said that, I did wonder if I would ever be able to; Priscilla seemed to be immersed in her own set. I went back to my room, hung up my suit and lay on my bed imagining men queuing up for Priscilla's attention, them dancing in their finery. But that was how things were and I just had to get on with life. I had enjoyed my day with Sir Miles; I thought he was the finest of men, part of that group of our finest who were decimated in the First World War even more than the Second. I just got on with work and looked forward to our Groupie gatherings. I probably belonged there as much as anyone.

A week later I had the sweetest note from Priscilla.

My Dear Bob,

Thank you so much for your lovely present. It is the nicest piece of jewellery I have. I will treasure it.

I am so sorry you did not make it to Hurlingham, but I quite understand. My father really enjoyed your company. He is so lonely since he lost Mother. Thank you.

A group of us are driving down to the south of France for a month. Aren't we lucky?

I hope to see you when we are back – do not work too hard.

Love, Priscilla x

I thought that this was just the conventional reply that her people wrote, but I put it safely away. How much or how little she meant in her letter, I treasured it as much as she said she treasured my birthday present.

CHAPTER SEVEN

A VERY HAPPY NEW YEAR

Just roll on hospital job. I would leave it for good and go into practice somewhere like the Somerset levels, where the starlings swirled around. I just had to hope. I wrote to a practice in Somerset and went down to see a delightful Dr Roger Ross and his wife Molly, and before I left I was told I could start there at the end of my House job that finished at the end of January.

I had a couple of postcards from Nice from Priscilla, saying 'We are having a lovely time here, wish you were with us', but no kisses. I would have loved being alone with Priscilla, but not with that chirpy crowd that hung around her.

Then a few weeks later, at the dentist's, I opened a new edition of the *Tatler* and there was a full page picture of Priscilla wearing the usual pearls. The text said, 'Priscilla Justin-Boyston, daughter of Colonel Sir Miles Justin-Boyston, announces her engagement to Major P J Tomkins-Brown with the wedding to be in

April next year.'

I had always thought that this would happen. I wrote a short note to her, congratulating her. Then two weeks later I had an invitation to her father's sixty-fifth birthday tea. Naturally, I accepted, and as it said 'dress informal', I set off on the day of the birthday in a sports coat and trousers. Of course, when I arrived there they were all wearing suits. Sir Miles greeted me like a long lost son and sort of raised his eyebrows.

Priscilla, looking absolutely gorgeous, came over with the good-looking tall Hussar. She said, 'Peter, this is my dear friend Bob. Bob this is my husband-to-be, Peter.'

'Hello, "Dear friend Bob",' said Peter, in a haughty voice. 'You are obviously very good at dressing informally.'

'Yes,' I replied. 'I am just a working lad. I think that you are a very lucky man; I had always had hopes myself.' As I said this, I could have sworn that Priscilla bit her lip and there was the beginning of a tear in her eye.

'Well,' he said, 'hard luck chum!'

Priscilla said, 'Thank you for coming, Bob. My father is very fond of you.'

'As I am of him,' I said.

I had scoured every second-hand shop and antique shop to get him an original sketch of some bygone artist and he obviously loved the one I got for him. I had, fortunately, pre-ordered a taxi and was relieved to hear that it had arrived. Sir Miles came to the door with me to see me off. 'Thank you for coming, Bob,' he said.

'I do hope they are happy.'

'I hope so too,' he said. 'You are always welcome here.'

'I won't forget that.'

'Don't,' he said. So I got in my taxi and was pleased to get back to the hospital. I thought that that was the end of it all. This was September; at the beginning of December my father invited me to a father and son's night at the Savile Club and the first people we bumped in to were Sir Miles and Mark. They gave me the warmest of greetings. My father and Sir Miles went off droning to each other about the Sketch Club, whilst Mark and I went to the bar for a drink. 'How's the wedding preparations going?'

'Didn't you know?' said Mark. 'Priscilla broke off the engagement almost six weeks ago.'

'Good, I didn't really like him.'

'Neither did we,' Mark replied.

'Why did she back off?'

'She obviously preferred someone else.'

'Do you know who? Is it somebody already married?'

'No definitely not. Do you know who my father and I think it is?'

'No, I have no idea.'

'We,' Mark said, 'both thought it was you.'

'Not a chance. Priscilla is premier division; I am just second or third division south.'

'That's utter rubbish,' said Mark. He seemed cross.

Then we all went into dinner. As traditionally you only talk to the people either side of you at the club, I did not speak to them again. Except as they were going, I spoke to Mark for a second and said, 'Please give my love to Priscilla.'

'Sure,' he replied in a dismissive way.

I went back to my father and Louise's for the night, then back to the hospital the next day. Thank God, just Christmas and New Year to be got through, then down to be a GP in Somerset at the end of January.

All the Groupies were to go away for Christmas and as they settled in our meetings were less frequent.

I knew Christmas was going to be tough. I was covering for half the hospital and this, of course, was my thing. New Year's Eve was going to be worse; as far as I could see, I would be covering for the whole hospital. I said, 'I can't cope with the children's ward', but I knew I would have to. Christmas wasn't too bad, as various people came in and carved turkeys on the wards. On New Year's Eve I had an early dinner and went to lie on the bed for an hour. I had only just laid down when there was a knock at the door. There was Priscilla, dressed to the nines, clutching a bottle of champagne and wearing my moonstone. She looked terrific.

'What a lovely surprise,' I exclaimed. 'You look absolutely lovely and you are wearing my moonstone.'

'Yes,' she said.

'You said in your letter that it was your favourite piece of jewellery. I thought that was the type of letter that your sort wrote.'

'For heaven's sake, Bob,' and she was near to tears, 'there isn't an "our sort" and "your sort" we are all just people.'

I said, 'I am sorry about your engagement.'

'I'm not, he was a prick.' It was a sign of desperation.

'I'm sorry,' I replied. 'Where are you off to?'

'The family New Year's party.'

'Please give my best wishes to Mark and your father.'

'Yes. I must fly.' She handed me the champagne. 'I want you to promise that you will drink this at the stroke of midnight.'

'I will, if I can.'

'No,' said Priscilla, 'definitely drink it then,' and she shot off to my rather weak 'Happy New Year' and she was gone.

The night was murder. Half an hour after she left I was on the run right on into the night. I looked at my watch; it was twenty minutes to twelve and I had to finish the stitching I was doing. I said, 'You will have to call someone else in. I'm just about done for.'

I got back to my room at five to twelve to find Priscilla sitting there holding the champagne. She was looking doleful.

'What a nice surprise! What's happened?'

She wailed a dismissive sort of, 'Shut up! Have you any glasses?'

'I'm afraid not, but I can find two clean mugs.'

'Bob, you are hopeless.'

I poured out the champagne just as New Year struck. We both took a sip and she burst into tears. 'Bob,' she said, 'it's Leap Year, for God's sake, please marry me and put me out of my misery! I have loved you ever since we first said "Hello". My heart used to nearly leap out of my chest when you came into the medical school restaurant. I used to walk past your table of Rugby Buggahs or found you were helping people climb over stiles.'

I, too, was openly weeping now. 'Priscilla, my love, this is always the way I have felt about you. I didn't think I stood a chance. May I kiss you?'

'Bob, you are impossible. Please come and hug me nearly to death. We have a lot of living to do.'

We clung together – I just inhaled her. This was every dream I had come true. She sat on my knee and we kissed and caressed. I said, 'Aren't I supposed to first ask your father?'

'No, he nearly came round to ask you himself.'

I looked at her lovely face and said, 'I will cherish you,' and she replied, 'just as I will cherish you. I always wondered, watching you, if you were a missionary or something. If you are, and want to go to Africa or India or somewhere, I won't mind, as long as I am with you.'

'How strange you should say that – I had, when much younger, thought of being a Missionary Doctor in China, and the China Inland Mission said they would help pay my medical school fees, and all sorts of people were on their knees praying for me. But I was very young, and even before I went mining, I started to question things and found that I could not have one philosophy for life and another for religion. So I have left religion behind, although I respect all religions. I just have my own philosophy. I'm sorry to disappoint you about Africa, but I am due to start as a GP in Somerset at the end of the month.'

'Oh darling, that will be absolutely marvellous.'

'What about your neurology?'

'Oh, that can go off with your religion. I want to be your partner as a GP, as well as being your partner in everything.'

I had a sudden thought. I got up and went to a drawer and pulled out a little box. I said, 'My mother went off with someone and then they were both killed in a car accident.'

'I know,' she said, 'my father told me.'

'The only thing that I was left is her engagement ring. Would you like to wear it until I get you a proper one?'

She looked at it. 'Oh Bob, I would love to have it.'

I put it on her finger; it fitted perfectly.

'Bob, I would love to keep this as my engagement ring, it somehow makes me one of the family.'

I said, 'Do you mind if I ring my father?'

'Darling,' she said, 'I don't mind what you do. Will they be up?'

'Yes, still partying.'

I rang my father. 'Dad, I have just got engaged.'

'That's tremendous,' he said. 'Louise. Bob has just got engaged.' They both came to the telephone and said, 'Is Priscilla still with you?'

'I said, 'How do you know it's Priscilla? Have I ever mentioned her?'

'Yes,' they both said, 'you hardly talk about anything else. Can we speak to her?'

'Priscilla, my father and Louise would like to talk to you.'

'Hello,' she said.

I could hear my father and Louise. 'Welcome to the family.' Louise said, 'Welcome daughter-in-law' and Priscilla said something about 'He will be on his own'; I hoped that didn't mean me. Then Priscilla turned back to me. 'Bob, your father wants another word with you.'

'Bob. Had you thought of giving Priscilla your mother's engagement ring?'

I said, 'I have already.'

'I'm so pleased for you. We knew that this was going to happen eventually.'

'Well, I didn't. It all seems too good to be true. Has this wait of seven years been my fault?'

'No,' said my father, 'you are probably only now just ready for each other. You used to get your mind locked into so many things.'

'The only thing I have been locked into these last years, is Priscilla.'

'Yes. Go and enjoy each other. See you later.'

'Okay, Dad. I could well eat her before breakfast.' I put the phone down.

'Who might eat who before breakfast?'

I said, 'I might eat you.'

'Oh great,' she said, 'please start.'

I sat in my old armchair. She sat on my knee and cuddled up. We kissed, caressed, inhaled each other. I sat back. Was this all really happening? This was my dream come true.

'Bob,' she said, 'this was always going to happen.'

'I wish somebody had told me.'

Priscilla continued, 'I was in despair. I said to my father, "What do I do? Do I have to go and propose to him?" "Maybe," he said. I asked, "Why doesn't he just come and ask me?" He said, "I think you are beyond his concept." I said, "What does that mean?" He replied, "Having said that, I think he probably thinks that it would be too disrespectful to approach you direct. He did say that you were the loveliest, finest thing on two legs. He said he adores you." I said, "That doesn't stop him having a one-legged girl, who he has just found God for. Do you know he has a group of displaced doctors in his room each night?"'

'Priscilla, darling,' I said, 'we are now past all that.'

She clung to me. 'Bob, I think you would have made a very naughty missionary.'

'Why?'

'Well I can feel something stirring in the undergrowth.'

'Oh, that must be my friend; he is longing to meet you.'

'And I'm longing to meet him,' said Priscilla. She then took my face in her hands, she said 'My Love, I am yours completely and you can take me completely – now, tomorrow or whenever. I am just longing for you. But, things have been going at such a pace, if we could wait until we are married I think it would make it more special.'

'God, I have dreamed of it,' I said. 'Can we get married this afternoon?'

'You are an idiot! What do you really think?'

'I can't think any more. I don't think that I can wait more than six months.'

'How strange,' she said, 'that's what I thought and, of course, we have to take father's views. Oh, Bob, he doesn't know where I am and of course he doesn't know about us yet. The party will shut off at 1.00 am. What time is it now?'

'12.45.'

'Do you mind if I ring him now?'

'Of course not.'

Somehow the last three-quarters of an hour seemed to have been a lifetime. She was concentrating on her call. 'Father, it's Priscilla.'

I heard him say, 'Thank God you're safe!' Then, 'Where are you?'

'I am at Bob's hospital.' Then with a little catch in her voice she said, 'We have just become engaged.' Then she gave a sort of gasp. 'What's happening? Are you okay?' And nothing back.

Then suddenly Mark was on the telephone. 'It's okay, I think his cup just runneth over. We are sitting him down and giving him a whisky. Well,' he said, 'at last you two idiots have got together. Can I speak to my brother-in-law? Hello Second Division South, are you going to rise up the league or do we have to come down?'

'Mark,' I said, 'I do apologise.'

'Rubbish, you have been a member of the family as long as I remember. Now, how is my young sister getting home?'

'A taxi, or whatever.'

'No,' said Mark, 'I will come over to the hospital in about an hour. I know father will not go to bed now until he has seen her. Do you know he is on his own for lunch today?'

I said, 'Priscilla is going to bring him over to my father's for lunch.'

'That's absolutely great.'

In the hour we waited for him, we planned about another ten years. I said, 'Are you sure you don't want to be a neurologist?'

'No,' said Priscilla, 'I shall put in my months' notice tomorrow. I am going to be your GP partner.'

'Not without an interview.'

'Can I have the interview now?'

'Yes. Stand up. Yes, I think you will do.'

'We will be *P & B Ramsden, GPs.*'

'Yes, I have to be down in Somerset at the beginning of February and I have all kinds of things I have to sort out; like a driving licence, a car, whatever …'

'I can drive us down,' said Priscilla.

'That's great.' I had almost forgotten that I had to start out into the great wide world. We heard Mark's car drive up to the hospital and, holding hands, went down to meet him. He embraced both of us. 'So pleased. I think this is going to be the best year ever.'

'Yes,' I said after a last hug goodbye. I went up to my bed, fell into it fully clothed and had the deepest night's sleep I had ever had.

I was woken by church bells welcoming in the New Year – somehow my grotty old room seemed to shine. I just had to inhale, and the scent of Priscilla seemed to flow into me. I had a bath, shaved and went down for breakfast. When I arrived the whole of the Groupie lot were there waiting for me. They had a huge parcel with them. Henry was the spokesman. 'Bob,' he said, 'a small present from all of us.'

'What's this for?' I asked.

'It's your engagement present from us.'

'How did you know I was engaged?'

'There are no secrets in hospitals.' He went on, 'Bob, on behalf of all of us, we wish you every possible happiness, and we all wanted to thank you for being our anchor while we have been lonely and away from our loved ones.'

I undid the big present, which had about ten wrappings, to find it was a twenty-pound tin of Indian spices. I was very touched. I mumbled back my gratitude and thanked them for steadying my step.

I picked up my father and Louise's Christmas presents from my room, then rang for a taxi that took me over to my father's. They seemed to be as excited as I was. I was like a cat on hot bricks waiting for Miles and Priscilla to arrive. Priscilla was driving.

Miles and I embraced. 'Welcome to the family, Bob. You two say your hellos; I will go up to Andrew and Louise.'

I said, 'Hello exquisite wife-to-be.'

She replied, 'Hello, muscular husband.'

This lovely beautiful girl came into my arms. I said, 'This is my first taste of paradise.'

'Bob, my love, there is a great deal more to come.'

I don't think there was any possible way things could have been better. There was the warmth of Miles, my father and Louise. There was champagne and laughter. Priscilla and I kept in touching distance of each other. This beautiful lovely happy girl was apparently mine.

I had to break away for a minute. I needed to go to the toilet. I stood at the window looking out on the manicured gardens of those luxury apartments. I thought, *Yesterday morning I awoke to face a dull day, with a bright spot on the horizon being I would be leaving the hospital in four weeks, and starting in general practice in Somerset. Suddenly there is this massive changing to everything I had never thought possible.*

I remembered a lecture by Christopher Fry. I had toyed with the thought of combining medicine with writing and had been taken as a guest to the PEN Writers' Day, the international writers' organisation in the Purcell Room on the South Bank. The main speaker was Christopher Fry and his paper was 'Looking for a Language'. There was a phrase: 'the sensation of overtaking something that has always been waiting for you.' *Good for Christopher!* I thought.

When I got back Priscilla said, 'Are you okay, love?'

'Yes, I was thinking about something that Christopher Fry said.

'Oh,' she said, 'I hoped you would be thinking about me.'

'Of course. I never stop.'

'What did Christopher Fry say?'

'He said, "The sensation of overtaking something that's always been waiting for you", and it appears I have.'

'Oh. I see what he – you mean.'

'I have been such an idiot.'

'Of course, you have,' she said. 'That's part of why I love you so much.'

We had the loveliest of days. I couldn't keep my eyes off Priscilla; she always conducted herself beautifully and elegantly.

I had a moment in the kitchen with Louise, a wise, much-travelled artist and sculptor. 'Bob, she is quite perfect, completely exceptional. You two are going to have the best life ever.'

I agreed. 'I'm so lucky.'

'Bob,' she said, 'you are both fortunate and there was never any doubt that you two would finish up together.'

'Louise, this is the first time you have met her. How long have you known all this?'

She smiled. 'From the first time you came back and said oh, so casually, "Oh, I met a very nice man with a really lovely daughter today." Andrew said to me, "That will be the one." You are a one-woman man, Bob and there is no doubt that Priscilla is a one-man woman. Andrew and I are so delighted.'

'I did have a date once.'

She said, 'What happened to her?'

'She didn't turn up.'

Louise laughed. 'Bob, don't you dare touch another dish. Get back to your love.'

We wanted to get married in the chapel at Boyston Hall with a marquee on the lawn for the Wedding

Breakfast. We did not want an engagement party, or stuff in the *Tatler*, etc., our engagement was so special. I could see Miles was getting a bit tired. My bride-to-be came over and nuzzled me. 'My darling, we have to go.'

I said, 'Help, don't leave me!'

She gave me a smile. 'I'll come over to St Olive's for lunch tomorrow. Not in that awful hospital dining room. If I bring some sandwiches, what culinary delights can you offer? And I am not keen on Ovaltine at lunchtime.'

'What about tomato soup?'

'Perfect, I will try to make it about 1.00 pm.'

We had a long hug in a place behind the flats, then they went.

I slept at my father's for the night, then went into the hospital in the morning. As the taxi took me in, I reflected that I only had to spend three more weeks there, as I was owed a weeks' holiday. I did my ward round a bit on auto-pilot, with everybody congratulating me on my engagement. I was back in my room at 12.30 pm. The tomato soup was in the pan on the gas ring. When Priscilla arrived at nearly 1.00 pm she came into the room and said, 'Was it only yesterday morning we became betrothed?'

'No,' I said, 'we have been betrothed for years.'

'Perhaps you are right.'

We were lying on the rug, watching the tomato soup heat up, when there was a knock at the door. I shouted, 'Come in!' and in came a bespectacled hospital administrator. He said, 'Dr Ramsden, you know that you are not allowed to have females in your room.'

I felt my hackles rise. In a loud firm voice I said, 'How dare you! This is my fiancée, Dr Justin-Boyston. I have three weeks to go here; I can easily be out of here tonight.'

He started to mumble apologies.

I said, 'Just get out,' and pushed the door on him.

'Oh!' said Priscilla, laughing. 'I love it when you are masterful.' She smiled. 'Remember my Senior Neurologist Registrar?'

'Yes. I was worried about myself there. I felt I could easily have killed him.'

'Yes,' agreed Priscilla, 'I think that he felt that too.'

She asked, 'Where did you get that dreadful shirt tail story from? I hope you don't use it too often.'

'Never again,' I said. 'It happened underground; the overman, the underground manager, was having a slanging match with a collier who came out with it. I thought I will save that one; one day I will be able to use it. So, I did, and it's put away now.'

'That's good news,' said Priscilla.

'Any other masterful occasions?' I ventured.

'Yes, when you made that try that won the hospital cup; you had men bouncing off you like flies. I was so proud.'

I said, 'I was completely knackered. As somebody threw the ball to me, at that moment I got a flash of your face screaming, "Come on, Bob". So you turned my supercharger on and it was you who was really responsible for it all.'

'In hindsight, I did feel we had in some ways communicated,' she said. 'I was really fired up and when the drips who always seem to surround me started shouting "come on the coal man", I was very angry.'

'What did you say?' I asked.

'I won't repeat all of it; it's a word I don't use. But I turned on them and said "You lot of drips", and the last word was "off".'

'Thank God.'

We managed to see each other most days for the next three weeks. Either she came to me, or I went to her. We were never troubled again when she came to my room. I made a point of going to see the official who had bothered us. I said, 'I do apologise; I appreciate you were only doing your job.'

He said, 'I am so pleased you said how you felt. We are reviewing the whole system. We think that in this day and age, Housemen can entertain whoever they want in their rooms.'

We shook hands and that was that.

We had a weekend at Boyston Hall. We also had a weekend at my father's, where he and Louise could not quite understand that although engaged we did not wish to share a bedroom at night.

I rang Dr Ross, the GP in Somerset, where we were heading, to tell him my good news. 'I am delighted, Bob,' he said. 'We were concerned that having a bachelor take over, every single woman between twenty and sixty would be after you. I am so happy that you and your wife are going to be GP partners. That's how my wife Molly and I were. She has not been practising medicine for a few years now. Patients will be delighted that they now have a choice between male and female again. When are you getting married?'

'June,' I answered.

'Great. You must take a month off and until then, you will both be salaried partners. When you come back, you will take over the whole practice, if you want to. We'll have to sort out the practice property; I will make sure that it is not a problem. It includes a two-bedroom flat that I put up locums in. You are welcome to use it until you find somewhere of your own, and don't forget I will always be available to help if necessary.'

Priscilla was delighted when I told her. She said, 'I don't think there has ever been a better year, so far.'

'I couldn't agree more,' I said.

'What fun we are going to have.'

At last it came time for me to leave St Olive's. I had to say goodbye to all the Groupies. They all said that they would always keep in touch, but only Henry ever did. He became something very high in the India Medical Services and on visits to England, would come and see us with his very tiny wife. Hallum went back to the Lebanon and I feared for him with all the troubles they always seemed to be having there.

I called a taxi and piled in all my accumulated possessions of the last two years. I waved St Olive's goodbye. It had been mainly good with occasional bad times. I went off to the Hall where they had given me a room of my own, and at last Priscilla and I were under the same roof.

It is impossible to describe the sheer joy of being together. After a few days we set off for Somerset, with Priscilla driving. She said, 'I will have to teach you how to drive.'

'No,' I replied, 'we will not want a divorce so soon in our relationship.'

'I see what you mean. Perhaps a driving school is the best.'

'You do know I am a bit thick.'

'Who knows that better than me,' she said, giving my right knee a tweak with her left hand.

CHAPTER EIGHT

WEDDING BELLS

I would have quite happily settled with Priscilla driving me, (particularly when she had a hand on my knee) for several days at a time. Even though we travelled on country roads as far as possible, it only took a day to get down from London to the village of Plumstock in Somerset.

Plumstock was an old market town with a population of about six thousand. It had a weekly open market and cattle market. There was also a large pannier market where smallholders could bring produce to sell. It had a magnificent church that way back had been called Plumstock Cathedral. It was very much a dormitory town for Bath, and as Bath had continued to grow since Roman times, so Plumstock had shrunk until it stabilised a few hundred years ago. It gave up its claim to be a city.

Dr and Mrs Ross lived about two miles from the centre, close to the surgery. Roger and Molly gave us the warmest of welcomes at their beautiful Tinehead House, which was crammed with antiques. We were given a cream tea. I had met both of them briefly when I had come down for an interview, but even though Priscilla had only just met them, you would have thought, listening to us, that we were old friends. This was always how it was with her; she had the inbred quality of always being able to put people at their ease. When Molly and Priscilla went off to explore Molly's kitchen, Roger said, 'Bob, you certainly know how to pick a winner, she is just lovely.'

'Yes,' I agreed. 'I can hardly believe my good fortune; she is my wildest dream come true.'

'Well,' said Roger, 'I think that she has not done too badly herself. The practice is one of my "babies" and I am so relieved that I will be handing it over to you two.'

When the ladies came back, Roger drove us to the surgery. It was a single storey white stone building. I was surprised to see how big the premises were. Roger took us into a small office near the door. Inside there was a smiling, dumpy little lady. Roger introduced us. 'This is Helen, our Practice Manager. She is the heart of the practice and I can tell you she has the biggest heart in the county.'

'Ah, Doctor Roger,' she replied blushing. 'You always say those outrageous things about me. I am just a clerk. I am so pleased to meet my new employers.'

I replied, 'We are both delighted to meet the biggest heart in Somerset.'

'Oh help,' replied Helen. 'With Dr Roger going I thought that I had lost my tormentor. Please take pity on me Dr Ramsden.'

'I'll try,' I said.

'Now,' she said, 'can we all go and meet the rest of the team together? Dr Roger, there is a man here desperate to see you. I said you were not due to start for an hour. He said he would wait.'

'Okay, I'll see him. I'll let you show the young doctors round and meet the staff.'

Helen introduced us to the staff; two receptionists, a nurse and various district nurses. The surgery was surprisingly modern for this rural location. There was no doubt that it was Roger's 'baby' – no expenses seemed to have been spared on its equipment. There was a large waiting room, and two consulting rooms each with a separate examination room. There was a dispensary run by the nurse, a room for the health visitors and various ancillary helpers, and a treatment room where Roger and the nurse dealt with minor casualties. I thought it was a hell of a job the nurse did and, as if she had read my thoughts, Helen said, 'We actually have two nurses; one is on holiday.'

There were four rest rooms (toilets) – one male, one female, one for disabled and a small one for babies' nappy changing, etc. This was well ahead of its time. She then took us to the locum's flat, which was to be our temporary home. It was in walking distance of the surgery; it had a lounge-dining room, two bedrooms – one double, one single – a well-equipped kitchen-utility room, a bathroom with bath and shower, and a separate toilet room.

Then Roger took us back to our car. 'Today is Wednesday. I will give you a few days to settle in and you can start work on Monday. On Friday I have asked representatives of the surrounding practices for drinks and to meet you both. I am so pleased you have come here.' He kissed Priscilla, shook my hand and went off.

We got into Priscilla's car. She turned to me. 'I am so excited. I wonder if there are any shops still open. I have to feed my man.'

'Let's look round the flat first.'

Priscilla ran through the door and stood with arms open, and only when I went in cried, 'Bob darling, our first home', and we had the biggest hug ever.

We went into the kitchen and started to open cupboards and the refrigerator; it was like a Horn of Plenty. There was just about everything you could think of; two steaks for tonight, ham, bacon, eggs, butter, cheese, two fresh loaves of bread, milk, cream, cake and every tin of everything that included peaches, pineapple, peas, plums, sardines ... There was a profusion of vegetables in a vegetable rack and a bottle of wine.

'What is for tonight, darling? Sardines on toast?'

'Just the thing for you. I can easily eat two steaks.' We giggled. 'Now,' Priscilla said, 'sit down, husband, while your little wife prepares dinner.'

'Can I watch you?' I asked.

'Of course. And you can lay the table and pour us a glass of wine. Tonight's menu is steak and chips, peaches and cream, then coffee.'

Molly had made a huge effort preparing the flat for us. Priscilla said, 'I will take Molly some flowers tomorrow.'

Priscilla made a superb meal; it was difficult to imagine her doing anything badly. When we finished eating I said, 'Bedrooms. You must have the double one and I, the single. What a pity we can't share one. If were married, how it would cut the laundry down.'

'Yes,' said Priscilla. 'I would love to be a full wife. I am as eager as you are. Don't let's tease each other to death. If we can't hang on until we are married, it will not be a catastrophe.'

'I am going to try and stick to what we decided,' and rather disappointedly, 'I expect we will. But, I will bring you early morning tea.'

'Good. I will reward you with an early morning cuddle.'

We spent the next few days exploring the neighbourhood. On the Friday, all the local doctors seemed to be friendly. They gathered much more round Priscilla than they did me. She tried to keep me in touching distance and we held hands a lot. Most of the local doctors invited us to come and have a meal with them.

On the Saturday we went to Bath and had a look round that lovely city. I bought Priscilla some expensive binoculars, as she was interested in bird life. She bought me two silk ties, then lunch at a very nice restaurant. I remembered playing rugby against Bath and then de-muddifying ourselves in the warm water of a Roman bath.

I started taking morning tea in to Priscilla. I liked just to sit and watch her whilst she slept. A gentle kiss and two bare arms would meet behind my neck and she would pull me down to her. It is difficult to describe how lovely that was.

We just lazed about on the Sunday, and were both dressed, alert and ready to go at 8.00 am on the Monday. When we arrived at the surgery, Roger Ross and the staff were already there.

We settled into GP work. Of course, Priscilla was more popular than I was. All the women patients wanted to see her, as she was a woman, and nearly all the men wanted to see her because she was such a good-looking woman. So many of the patients who came to see me only came because they couldn't get in to see Priscilla.

I found as I started out as a GP that there were some differences between hospital medicine and general practice. One of my first patients came in complaining of an itchy bottom. This was not a condition which I had any instructions in treating. I suddenly remembered that my grandmother always had a tube of pile ointment in her bathroom. I fortunately remembered the name and prescribed it. Two weeks later, a delighted patient came back cured; I was the best doctor ever and he became a devoted patient.

I told Dr Ross who said, 'Bob, you will often find credit that you don't really deserve and complaints that you don't deserve, but in total you finish up with more credit than you deserve. It's not proportional.'

In hospital most patients had been seen by somebody before. I saw in general practice it was not always as clear cut; quite often there would be a preamble, 'Well, it's like this doctor, I was on the bus going to market and Mrs Jones said to me, "You look peaky, are you sure there is nothing wrong?" and I said, "Well, I do get a bit breathless if I hurry or walk uphill." "Well then," she said, "you ought to go and see Dr Bob Ramsden, he is good with older people. All the younger ones seem to choose his wife." I don't mean to be disrespectful, Doctor, but here I am.'

Then I would listen to her chest and take her blood pressure. She would, of course, shout with pain as the blood pressure taking cuff tightened and it would perhaps flash up that I would say she would probably be better off being ten or eleven stone rather than eighteen or nineteen. Of course no disrespect meant.

There was a not uncommon symptom in older ladies, who seemed to be my largest number of patients. They would sit down and gasp and say, 'It's my thingamy again, Doctor.' It could be up to fifteen minutes sometimes before I realised what their 'thingamy' actually was. It reminded me of the 'unt here' syndrome which seemed to be confined to plump women of eastern European extraction. It was usually some sort of abdominal pain and after examination of the piece of abdomen they had pointed to, finding nothing, I would say 'Anywhere else?' They would say, 'Here unt here, unt there.' In most cases there was nothing wrong at all and for some lonely ladies a trip to the doctor helped to break up the day. I did not mind that, it was part of being a family doctor. You would never dismiss any of them as just occasionally they had something seriously wrong with them.

I did get more than my share of elderly patients. Roger Ross was as good as his words, standing by us when needed. He assisted Priscilla when she gave an anaesthetic at a home birth, while I applied forceps to help the baby out the other end. He insisted on being on duty every other weekend too, to leave us free to get on with our wedding arrangements.

It was amazing how much time the wedding preparations took. We had to keep our numbers down to one hundred and twenty, which was the greatest number you can fit into the chapel at Boyston Hall. It seemed a lot of people to me. In fact, we could have found twice that number, most from Pricilla's side, but not a negligible number from mine. That included my father and Louise; my cousin George, an RAF pilot, and his wife Pamela; Mr Hines and his wife; Sid; Henry and various rugby friends; and Jack, one of the porters from St Olive's. Of course, Joyda was to be my Best Man and Irene a bridesmaid. Priscilla had to rush up to London, from time to time, for wedding shopping and fittings.

In odd moments when we had a bit of spare time, we had a look at some houses. Our favourite was a four-bedroomed Victorian house with a porch, wide entrance, a separate garage with an adjoining workshop, and a study on the end. The porch looked out over the Somerset Levels. We would love to have it. Could we afford it? We decided to wait until after the wedding before we went for it, hoping that it would still be on the market. Until then we enjoyed sharing the little flat, so looking forward to the time when we could share a bedroom. We made sure when we had our evening cuddles that we didn't get too carried away.

Although our spare time was absorbed with the wedding and house hunting, the main block of our time was taken up, of course, by general practice. I had been hugely helped by Mr Hines's approach of treating the 'whole patient'. Priscilla, despite not having had the benefit of working under him, slid naturally into this.

In spite of this, the wedding preparations did intrude. Priscilla came back from a rush up to London for a fitting, completely exhausted. 'Bob, darling,' she said, 'are you looking forward to the wedding?'

'Of course,' I said.

She raised her eyebrows. 'I am into your mind enough to know that is untrue.'

'You're right,' I replied, 'but there is no way I would let you down. My honest feeling is that it is something to be endured, but I have had other situations that I have had to endure when I have been surprised how things worked out. I shall be there for you; I will not let you down.'

'Bob, darling, I feel exactly the same as you. I'm afraid all I want is you. We could of course skip off to a registry office.'

'I know we could, but I know neither of us would. I have heard it quoted that you never enjoy your own wedding.'

'Oh! Bob, I am so pleased to hear you say that. We will just get through it together and, on the same subject, our honeymoon; you did suggest France, Italy and a quick trip to Ghent to see the Van Eyk polyptych of the Holy Lamb of the same place. It all sounds so exciting and I know that one day we will do all these things. But,' she said, 'we don't have to now. We are both physically naïve, we are both virgins. It will take us some time and practise to get completely to know each other.'

'I feel exactly the same as you. In fact, I had as a back-up plan The Sands Hotel in North Devon, which is a lovely hotel overlooking a long sandy beach. Their honeymoon suite is so far free on our dates.'

'Oh, lovely,' said Priscilla, 'please book it straight away. Oh how I love every fibre of you. Please hug me nearly to death.' We clung together and went further than we had ever been before; then the telephone rang.

'Oh, I hate that saying, "Saved by the Bell",' said Priscilla. 'I was ready to go all the way if it had not rung.'

'Yes,' I said, 'it was the same for me.'

'Bob,' she said as we picked up our medical cases, 'please let's share a bed tonight and not go further than we did just now.'

'I quite agree,' I said, 'it is all part of the learning process.'

Our 'saved by the bell' call was nothing serious, other than somebody needing reassurance, and it was surprising how often this was the only treatment required. In this case the patient had discovered what is called the xiphisternum, which is a small cartiligous lump in the middle and adjoining the bottom of the rib cage. We all have one.

From that night on we slept together but did not consummate our relationship. I always put my pyjamas on in my own room and Priscilla always had her nightdress on when I arrived. I had never seen her naked. 'That is going to be part of your wedding present,' she said, wickedly.

We worked hard to make sure all our guests were going to enjoy the wedding. Miles and my father had really pushed the boat out for the Wedding Breakfast. Miles had opened the whole of the Hall for the guests.

Both Miles and my father had sent generous cheques for the wedding presents, which meant that we could put a deposit on our Victorian house, which was called Khartoum Villa, providing it had not been sold.

By the time we got back to work all the invitations from surrounding practices were put off until post-wedding. We were busy at work, and before we knew it, June was just a week away. There were all sorts of pre-wedding parties, even though we had only been there for four months. Patients showered us with presents. Happily, Roger and Molly Ross were able to get cover for the wedding.

We set off for Boyston Hall on the first of June; this gave us six days before the wedding to, as it were, put the icing on the cake. When we arrived at the Hall it was all activity, with men putting up the marquee and bunting, and fairy lights being festooned all over. The gardens were immaculate and extra benches, with multi-coloured umbrellas, had been put all over the place. Being June, there was every expectation that it would be a sunny wedding day.

Miles was running everything with military precision. In fact, he had arranged for a military band to play for the wedding and for the dancing in the evening. Miles and Mark embraced us and I met Mark's fiancée, a lovely girl called Gillian. Priscilla had met her before, but I hadn't. Gillian and Joyda's Irene were going to be Priscilla's bridesmaids. Joyda and Irene were to be married in September.

Mark took our cases in.

'You do realise,' said Priscilla, 'we have separate rooms for the next six nights.'

'Yes.'

She said with a mischievous grin, 'I will make up for it.'

I put my arm around her. 'Don't say such things, you are making my knees wobble.'

The next few days were turmoil, with caterers, dressmakers, a profusion of presents to open, morning suits to be hired, florists doing their stuff and guests coming to stay at the Hall. Joyda and Irene were staying at a hotel nearby. Joyda said, 'I went to Moss Bros this morning. The last time I was there was when Priscilla invited me to the ball. That just leaves two more things for you to do – Everest and the Prime Minister and you're not even an MP yet.' Irene was just like her photograph; she was very good-looking but, of course, not as good-looking as Priscilla.

Eventually the great day came. The sun was shining. The band had been playing and everything looked picture perfect. I was standing nervously just below the altar. Mark was acting as an usher. Almost on time the band started up; 'Here Comes the Bride'. Joyda briefly turned round. 'My God, Bob, she looks out of this world.' I wasn't sure quite what he meant. Then there was this beautiful white apparition beside me. I turned and looked at her. 'Do I know you?' I whispered.

'No!' she said.

'I'm just a stable boy,' I replied.

The service was a blur; I remember exchanging rings and there we were, with Priscilla on my arm. 'You asked me who I was; I am Mrs P Ramsden of Doctors P and B Ramsden GPs and this is the happiest day of my life.'

We only allowed the photographer fifteen minutes, then into the Wedding Breakfast. The marquee was a mass of flowers with white jacketed soldiers serving us food. As we went in, there were constant hugs and kisses. We managed to get something to eat and drink. Priscilla said, 'I have a confession to make.'

'It's okay, I know,' I said, 'you have already been unfaithful to me.'

'You idiot!' she said. 'I am quite enjoying all of this.'

'Me too. I am so pleased we came.'

She kissed me. 'You are quite hopeless.' A lot of people must have been watching us, as there was a round of applause. Priscilla curtsied. I bowed.

The breakfast seemed to stretch on into the evening. Joyda gave a good speech, of course, bringing in Everest and the Prime Minister. In addition, he related how he and Priscilla had gone to the Graduation Ball and he had wanted to take her a leek instead of a posy. Priscilla dug me with her elbow. She said, 'I felt sure that the gardenia he gave me was from you. Did you pay for his dinner jacket as well?'

I said, 'I plead the Fifth Amendment.'

Then the dancing. I, of course, danced the first dance with Priscilla. I looked at her and said, 'I love you so much.'

'Thank God for that! I thought I might be just a pick up,' she said. Then in a more sombre mood she added, 'My darling, lovely Bob, you could not possibly love me as much as I love you.'

'You're looking tired. Don't you think you ought to be in bed?'

She groaned. 'Please don't tease. This doesn't finish until one. We have to be the last ones to go. We have at least five more hours and I am dying to give you my wedding present. I hope you will like it.'

'I'm sure I will.'

We hardly saw each other over the next few hours. Then at last it was 1.00 am and everybody was going. We saw the last one off. Miles had gone to bed earlier.

'Let's go.' She gripped my hand tighter than she had ever gripped it before. As we went upstairs to what was called 'The Bridal Suite' she said, 'Quick, lock the door, and get your clothes off.'

I started to take off my jacket, waistcoat and shirt. I heard a flurry of clothes behind me. A rather tense Priscilla said, 'Please turn round, Bob.'

I was only half undressed when I turned to find Priscilla completely naked. 'Bob,' she said, 'this is my main present. I give every fibre of my body to you. I have waited for this moment for the last seven years.'

Priscilla looked beautiful naked. She was unbelievable. I said, 'I am just lost for words; you overwhelm me. I am so lucky.'

She sounded nervous and came over and said, 'Come on, let me help you with some of those buttons.'

I tore the rest of my clothes off and we both jumped into bed.

'Is this paradise?' I asked.

She said, 'No, but we could easily reach it during the next two weeks.' As we had predicted we were very unskilled at all this, but we did manage to please each other several times during the night. Then, exhausted, our bodies entwined together, we went to sleep.

I woke up to see sunlight streaming through the window and Priscilla sitting up in bed naked to the waist. She was so utterly beautiful. I reached out for her, 'Come here you lovely thing.'

'No, Bob, not now. Maud is going to arrive any minute.'

'Who is Maud?' I asked. 'And isn't the door locked?'

'No, I unlocked it. Maud is our oldest maid; she always brings up the "first morning breakfast". She did for my mother and father.'

There was a knock on the door. 'Quick, beneath the bedclothes. Come in Maud.' In came an old lady with a tray, which contained half a bottle of champagne, a rose, a pot of coffee, milk, two boiled eggs, toast and marmalade and, of course, two champagne glasses.

She said, 'Miss Priscilla and Doctor Bob may I wish you both every happiness.'

'Thank you so much,' said Priscilla. 'It is good that you keep this tradition. I do hope you can do the same for our children. We are only just waking up. Could you please put the tray on the table?'

As soon as she had gone, I jumped out of bed, locked

the door, then got back into bed. I gathered Priscilla into my arms and said, 'Mrs Ramsden, you are about to suffer an experience worse than death.'

'Oh good,' she replied, and in our own clumsy way we made love, clinging to each other like limpets, then lay back breathless. I said, 'I think that was the best yet!'

'I quite agree,' said Priscilla. 'It was tremendous. I think the future looks incredible; we are already doing better than we thought we would. I would now like some champagne and breakfast.'

'Are you sure you're okay?' I asked, as I went to get the tray.

'Never better, my lovely muscular man.'

I fetched the tray, got back into bed beside her, opened the champagne, then said, 'I have a toast.'

'Let me guess,' she said, 'happy moments, health and prosperity – love, life!'

'No, it is a farewell toast.'

'Neurology hospitals?'

'No, it is a farewell to virginity.'

'I will toast that,' she agreed, and we tucked into our breakfast. We were both hungry.

I asked, 'Could we have been doing that for the last seven years? I loved you from the moment I saw you.'

'I was the same as you, there is a family gene in love. My father was exactly the same. He was in the Army in India where life was so full with polo, shooting and fishing that women did not figure. One day, the regiment was collecting for an exercise up country, transported by a military train. It took a day to load up. When it was at last on the move, it was a slow starting. It would take fifteen minutes to clear the station. As he looked out of his compartment window, he said, like a bolt of lightning his eyes met those of a most beautiful, elegant woman. He jumped out of the slowly moving train, rushed up to her and said, "Will you marry me?" She replied, "Of course, but hadn't I better know your name?" "Of course," he said and gave her his card. Then, accepting hers, he jumped back on the moving train and, eighteen months later, they were married in Tunbridge Wells. She was lovely. I miss her as much as he does. He knew we would finish up together, even before me, if that is possible.'

'Thank God, we are together,' I said. 'Your father is a Sir, are you a Right Honourable?'

'No, Mark is. I am something much more important.'

'A duchess?' I enquired.

'No, much more important. Mrs Bob Ramsden.'

CHAPTER NINE

HAPPY HONEYMOON

Having finished our breakfast we lay snuggled together in bed, until I said, 'Darling we have to face the day.'

'Whatever you say, my muscular man, but could I have a request?'

'Granted.'

'Do you mind having your bath and getting dressed and then going down to meet your new family? I would like to get dressed in my "going away" gear, then follow you down.'

'Of course,' I said, 'but on condition that we bath together. Now we are married we have to be careful of water usage. Think of all those thirsty people in the Sahara.'

'Yippee!' said Priscilla. 'I thought you would never ask!'

To my surprise she followed that pattern for the rest of our lives, although she would undress with little encouragement, and sometimes with no encouragement at all, she always liked to get dressed alone. I never said, 'This is what your lot are used to; having your own dressing room.' I thought it probable the ladies had had dressing rooms for generations. I just made sure that she had her own dressing room as soon as it was possible. We could not linger in the bath – we had to finish our packing then drive down to Devon. So I climbed out of the bath reluctantly, leaving Priscilla wallowing in the water, got dressed and said, 'See you in two minutes.'

'Can you make it three please and a kiss before you go?'

I went down to be greeted by Miles, Mark and Gillian, who were sitting in the sunshine. 'Where is Mrs Ramsden?' they asked.

'Dressing,' I replied.

'Just like her mother!'

When Mark and Gillian had gone off into the garden, I said to Miles, 'I gather it was spontaneous combustion when you met your wife. How long ago did you think that Priscilla and I would get together?'

'I hoped from the moment you carried her suitcases when you and Priscilla met. She knew straight away; her engagement to the Hussar, I think, was just to get your attention. It did worry me though, she has been surrounded by admirers ever since she was fifteen, she is even lovelier than her mother.'

'I can hardly believe my good fortune.'

'Well,' said Miles, 'here she is!'

I turned to see Priscilla approaching, looking immaculate in a beautifully tailored red suit. She looked absolutely terrific. I said, 'Are you really mine?'

'Yes, every single cell and corpuscle.' She kissed me and then kissed her father.

We were joined by Mark and Gillian. 'My word!' said Mark. 'My little sister is not too unattractive after all! Is that your driving gear?'

'She can be waving to the public whilst I drive her down to Devon by special courtesy of the Plumstock School of Motoring. I passed my test two weeks ago.'

'With Honours?' queried Miles.

'Not exactly. The examiner said, "Confidentially I am bending the rules. Your beautiful wife-to-be is my doctor and I don't want her tired out. But, if she comes to any harm I will be after you." "Don't worry," I said, "I will take the greatest care of her."'

'But didn't Priscilla drive you both up from Somerset?'

Priscilla came and put her arm round me. 'Bob is a safe but very steady driver, if he had been at the wheel it would have taken us about three days to reach here and we would have missed the wedding.'

After coffee we finished packing, loaded up the car and set off to a shower of confetti. We had been driving for about an hour when Priscilla asked, 'We are safely married now, 'til death do us part and all that?'

'Yes, definitely,' I replied, 'but of course I am driving and it could be a very short marriage.'

'It won't. But knowing that everything is signed and sealed, I have a confession to make. I lied to you.'

'I know, you are actually 85 not 25.'

'No,' she said, 'much worse! When at St Olive's we met and I said that I did not know you were still there, I in fact knew exactly where you were. I had a great struggle to get onto the West End Neurological Unit. I only managed it because the Senior Registrar fancied me. Mr Hines and my father have some sort of connection. I was not spying on you; I just wanted to know where you were. I was worried when I heard that there was a beautiful Swedish girl on the House. That's why I said I would get engaged to Peter. It was unkind of me, but I thought it might spur you on. There has only ever been one man for me and that's you.'

'That's strange,' I said. 'She was one of the Groupies who came to my room and she hinted that she could offer me all sorts of pleasures and I wondered, why not? Then a picture of lovely you seemed to appear and I was not interested. The only person I have ever wanted was you, but I can't explain it. I felt that it was far too presumptuous of me to approach you. You were always surrounded by people from your sort of background. Thank God you did what you did. I wonder what would have happened if you had not come?'

'Bob darling, I was always going to keep you in my sights, if you were in a relationship or got married I would have backed off. Whether I would have got married if you had, I really don't know. I have had proposals from men aged 18 to 80. I just wanted you. I felt I meant something to you when you went for my Senior Registrar like a tiger, and the night we went to the Royal Institution I thought all my dreams were coming true. Then it all seemed to go blank. I was really depressed. By the time New Year's Eve came round I was prepared to make a fool of myself. My main worry was that you would have just been kind to me. Am I forgiven?'

'Of course, you are. What an ass I have been. My father and Louise used to say that I never talked about anything but you.'

'My father said, "just keep on hanging in there, I want him as my son-in-law".'

'Our fathers were friends, do you think they discussed us?'

'No, neither of them are like that.' She continued, 'I am so pleased to get that off my chest.'

'I never mind seeing you taking things off your chest.'

'Okay,' she said and started to unbutton the jacket of her suit.

'Help!' I said. 'Not when I'm driving! Why not try

and doze so that you will be fresh for tonight.' I said, 'I will love you until your socks fall off!'

'I have never heard that before.'

'I know I have just invented it.'

'Great! We'll share that phrase. I am going to try and doze off as you suggested. Find a nice spot for a picnic in about a couple of hours. As this has been confession time, can you remember way back a medical school and your father's chauffeur Hunter came to pick you up and called you "Master Robert", and said you must not keep your father waiting, or something like that. What was said?'

'He really embarrassed me when we got into the car. He said "you fancy her don't you?" And I replied, "Yes, but she is premier division and I am second division south." He said, "Bollocks!" and I said, "How dare you speak to Master Robert like that!" He said, "All I can think of to reply is to say Bollocks again," then we both laughed.'

'I knew he was my sort of man. He said exactly the right words. What a pity he could not come to the wedding.'

'No,' I said. 'He is still in hospital – something he got in Korea, I gather. He should get better.'

'Good! We must invite him to come and see us.'

She put her head back and dropped straight off to sleep. I would steal a glance at her from time to time as we drove along. She still looked beautiful and elegant even when she was fast asleep. I think she must have created the phrase 'drop off to sleep'. I found over the weeks, months, years that she had the ability just to put her head down and be asleep in a couple of minutes.

After two hours I took a minor road off the main one and drove around until I found a nice field by a stream, took out a car rug and spread it on the grass. Then I got out the huge hamper that the kitchen at Boyston Hall had made up for us. Priscilla was still fast asleep. I opened the car door and awoke her with a kiss. As I did this, she put her arms round my neck and pulled me tight to her. 'Dear lovely muscular Bob, I am so happy.' I almost lifted her out of the car and we made our way to the rug. She opened the hamper.

'Oh!' she gasped. 'There is enough food here to last us a week!' It included half a bottle of champagne and a thermos of coffee. I think that much of the food was surplus from the wedding breakfast, but it was delicious – we did not open the champagne. It was difficult to resist the temptation. We stuck to coffee and cold food.

With my driving, we did not reach the hotel until about 9.00 pm. The hotel was absolutely lovely, looking down on this glorious stretch of sand. We were shown to our suite, which was beautiful and had a balcony overlooking the beach. The manager said the restaurant was still open or he could send some food up to our room.

I said, 'We have enough food to feed the whole hotel. What we would like is a champagne bucket and ice and two champagne glasses.' We were both very tired by now, and hot and sweaty – at least I was. We unpacked our clothes. Priscilla had brought enough for a month. My wardrobe was very modest beside it.

We showered separately, and wearily put on the linen dressing gowns the hotel had provided. Whilst I had been having my shower, Priscilla had laid out food from the hamper. I opened the champagne, poured it into the two glasses and we drank to 'our immense good fortune'. We were not very hungry but ate some food, packed up the rest, slipped our dressing gowns off, clung together and – we both fell asleep. I slept soundly.

We woke up at the same time, almost startled to find that we were in bed together. I said, 'Good morning, darling,' as I kissed her on the forehead. 'Good morning, Mrs Ramsden.'

She wrapped her arms around me. 'Good morning, Muscle Man. Tell me, what happened last night?'

'I thought I had got into bed with a wild woman from Borneo. I nearly rang reception; I was scared for my life. You tore my back to shreds with your nails.'

'My love, I am so sorry. I just can't remember. Let me look at your back.' I turned my back to her. 'There is not a mark on it! I know we actually both slept solidly throughout the night. You rotter, you had me worried. I have a good mind to lacerate your back now!'

We made love in our naïve, unsophisticated way, then lay back cuddling.

'As we had a busy day yesterday, could we have breakfast in bed?' asked Priscilla.

'Of course.' I rang reception. 'Two full English breakfasts with tea, please.'

'How did you know that I wanted a full English breakfast?' Priscilla queried.

'I just knew.'

'You were right. I could eat a horse!'

'I don't think they serve horse for breakfast. It is not on the menu. You will have to put up with bacon, egg, tomato, black pudding, toast and marmalade.'

We wolfed it down, finishing every scrap. This was the first time we had relaxed in weeks. We both fell asleep, still entwined around each other.

North Devon had so many places to explore. At the lovely town of Bideford, Scandinavian Timber Boats were moored at the quay. There was no railway there, everything had to be unloaded by crane onto lorries.

There were towns with histories going back to whenever. We went to Barnstaple with its Pannier Market and Butchers' Row; the remnants of Imperial

College where Kipling had been to school; Pebble
Ridge, that great ridge of pebbles which keeps the sea
out of the Northern Burrows common land. And
Westward Ho!; the only town to be named after a book.
We swam there, and were amazed at the strength of the
undertow. I would not let Priscilla swim out too far. It
was much the same at Croyde Bay, but most of the other
beaches were benign.

One day we got up very early and climbed to the top
of Dunkery Beacon on Exmoor, arriving just before
dawn, then sitting there as a wonderful view came into
sight. We could see Barry Docks clearly. Then down to
Minehead for breakfast. There were so many places we
visited; Ilfracombe, Torrington – where we bought some
glass; Appledore – where in the old parts the very
narrow roads had gutters running down the middle,
which enabled the residents, way back, to empty their
chamber pots from their bedroom windows to the gutter
below. It must have smelt a bit frisky in those days.
Thank goodness for flush toilets and mains drainage!

We caught a boat from Appledore to Instow, where
we sat and got a panorama of Appledore, its ship
building yards and the life boat bobbing on its mooring,
with the whole of the Torridge Estuary pouring into
what we understood was Bideford Bay if you come from
Bideford, or Barnstaple Bay if you come from
Barnstaple, where the river Taw makes its contribution
to the bay. We learned that both Bideford and Barnstaple
sent out boats to fight against the Spanish Armada.

We liked Croyde Bay, but were put off by the number
of caravans there. There were some glorious beaches;
Saunton Sands, where we were staying; Putsborough
and, of course, Westward Ho! and Instow. Most often
we came down for breakfast, went out for a swim and
then did not appear until the evening. Of course Priscilla
had a different dress to wear each night. I ran out of

adjectives to describe how she looked.

Apart from the people in reception, and the waiters, we did not talk to anyone in the hotel. There were obviously two or three other honeymoon couples who were staying; you could tell by their pale faces and the rings around their eyes. We could never get enough of each other. We did not like either one of us going out of each other's sight. We talked most of the time, or nearly all the time, and with our excursions in the sun and sea, Priscilla bronzed beautifully. I of course, went red with a peeling nose.

We just about explored the whole of North Devon and each day we walked and swam on top of everything else we did. Physically we became completely in tune.

The days, nights and mornings passed too quickly and the end of the honeymoon was approaching. We had sent off as many cards as we could; bought some presents for Miles, Mark and Gillian, my father and Louise. When we finally left the hotel, having over-generously tipped just about everybody in sight, it was not with a heavy heart. There was no way it could have been better than it was. The staff, especially after being tipped said, 'Do come and see us again.' But we knew we wouldn't. Any return would be an anti-climax.

CHAPTER TEN

BACK TO WORK

We had a week before starting work again, but we were both very keen. We also hoped Khartoum Villa was still on the market. When we got back to our flat we found that it was stuffed with even more presents. We went to the estate agents as soon as we could on the Monday. The villa still had not been sold, so we immediately made an offer, subject to a survey.

We then set about writing thank you letters. We went up to Boyston Hall for two nights; one night at my father's and then back on the Friday for work on the following Monday. We had managed to bring most of our presents back with us and a promise from Miles that we could take away what we wanted, from rooms stored with lovely Victorian furniture, for our new house. That was, of course, if we got it. We sorted out most things over the weekend, then arrived at the surgery together at 8.00 am on the Monday.

At the surgery we were greeted with applause from

the staff and patients. We were inundated with work. Many people had chronic ailments and had waited a month to see us, mainly Priscilla of course, but quite enough for me as well.

Roger and Molly Ross invited us for first dinner and then the formal handing over of the practice. We were both apprehensive; this was a big deal, not least how heavily financially committed were we going to be. We had seen a bank manager in Bath who assured us that he was used to this sort of deal and that it shouldn't be a problem. But we were stepping into the unknown. When the bank manager said, 'It should not be a problem', did he mean for him or us?

Molly had, of course, laid on a lush spread. I could see us being there all night. We eventually finished this lovely meal. 'Now,' said Roger, 'down to business.' He went off and fetched a huge pile of papers.

'Take them to a solicitor and get them to sort out the details. I have been as generous as I can. We were never able to have children so the practice was my baby and I was able to help it grow. It is such a comfort to know that I am handing it over to two pairs of safe hands. You are both too old for me to adopt you, but as long as I live, I shall always try to be a sort of in loco parentis. Never ever hesitate to get in touch if there is a problem.'

I stood up. 'First, I would like to thank Molly for this sumptuous feast, and for the way she stocked up the locum's flat for us. It will be a difficult standard to maintain, we may have to call you in as a consultant. Roger, we both know you're certainly the most generous person we have ever met. Without having seen the details of our purchase of the practice property, we know it will be loaded in our favour. We will do our very best with your baby and hope we can make it grow. We have little to offer back, but be sure that you have two caring doctors who will do their best to take care of you both while you are still alive.'

Both Roger and Molly had tears in their eyes. It was all kisses and handshakes. As we were about to leave Roger said, 'Wait I have a small present for you.'

The small presented looked like a wide board about six feet long. He passed it over and said, 'Open it when you get home.'

Before we left I said to Roger, 'Thank you both for this surprise present. There is one thing I would like to ask; had you any guiding principle as a family doctor?'

'Yes,' said Roger, 'I did have and as far as I can see you are both heading in the same direction. When I see a patient I make sure that I consider the whole patient. When they come in I don't say straight away "What's wrong?" I first ask them about where they live, what sort of family they have, what work they do, the name of their dog and where they go on holiday. Only then do I ask them, "How can I help you?"'

'You sound like Mr Hines.'

'I'm afraid I don't know Mr Hines.'

'He was my consultant surgeon for my first House job. He said try and do a social round each day; go round to patients – don't talk about their medical condition, just talk to them in the way you described.'

'I thought I might be talking to the converted; one Sermon on the Mount is enough. Now off and open your present.'

The floor of the sitting room was cleared. We took the cover off one side of what looked like a board. It turned out to be plain Formica. 'Perhaps it's a symbolic diving board, as we are jumping in the deep end,' Priscilla said. 'We ought to turn it over.'

We did and she gasped, 'Another dream come true.'

There in beautiful gothic script it read *P and B Ramsden, Family Doctors.*

'Let's put it up now.'

We carefully unscrewed the old sign and screwed on ours, which was the same size. 'I think we Doctors Ramsden should go to bed. We have a lot of hard work before us.'

We were quite tired and wine had flowed freely all evening. We lay in bed holding hands, both a bit subdued. I said to Priscilla, 'I know what you are thinking.'

She replied, 'And I know what you are thinking. For the first time in our medical lives, apart from each other, we are on our own. We are the only medical source available for several thousand people.'

'This is what we spent all those years working for. I cannot think of a better team. We can only do our best, and our best is going to make us the best practice in the area. Patients in other practices will all wish they were with us.'

'Bob, darling, you always have the right words. How could I ever manage without you?'

'There is no chance of that. We are welded together – two minds in tune. We will take care of our flock. Do you know what I want to do next?'

'Yes, let's go to sleep and be fresh for tomorrow.'

We slept soundly and awoke early. As we approached the surgery, hand in hand, there were lots of cars about. It looked as if we were in for a busy time. When we were in the door, we saw the room was packed with everybody connected to the surgery; apart from nurses and receptionists, there were midwives, the health visitor, the social worker and even the cleaner. There was applause as we went in. This was our second standing ovation. We were greeted by Helen, the practice manager. She said, 'This is an early morning welcome party. There are no patients until 10 am.' We were introduced to everyone. Some we already knew, we tried to make mental notes of who was who. Having done the rounds, Helen then took us over to an iced cake on a table in the corner. 'We were not sure what to call you and this is what we came up with.'

She whipped off the cover and there in big letters was *Dr P And Dr Bob*. To Helen's embarrassment, Priscilla laughed. 'I am so sorry but Dr P makes me sound like a urine test. I can see people saying I am off for a pee. That would mean they are coming to see me. Some people call me Prissy, which I hate. Priscilla is too long. Could I settle for Dr Ramsden?'

Fortunately Helen laughed too. 'I am so sorry. We had not thought of that. Dr Ramsden it will be.' But from then on, when Priscilla and I were alone, I called her Dr P.

At last the cake was eaten, and the staff went off to their various work places. I do not think they had heard of Dr Roger's complete retirement; it had not been publicised. There was to be no formal retirement or retirement party. When questioned, he said, 'You are retaining me as a consultant.'

'How much do you want in the way of payment?'

'£1 each Christmas.'

'Done!' I said. What it really meant was that although he had handed his baby over to us, he did not want to let it go completely.

The surgery started on time. My first lot of patients were unremarkable; off work certificate, cystitis, earache, tonsillitis. You are not allowed to fall in love with patients. But I'm afraid I did with the next one. He was a little old man who walked as if his knees were tied together. He shuffled in and said, 'With Roger gone, I have to find another doctor. What do they call you?'

'Bob. What is your name?'

'Jack.'

'Jack who?'

'Jack Bottom. Now,' he said, 'what do my friends call me?'

'I would say, Jack Arse.'

'Well done,' he said. 'That's a good start. You can be my doctor.'

'Steady,' I said, 'I am very selective.'

'Bugger off, people only come to you because they can't get in to see your wife.'

I said, 'She is better looking than me.'

'Yes,' he said. 'She is a stunner. As head of the local Mafia, if anybody bothers her they will be dead before they know what hit them.'

'How many are there in the local Mafia?'

'Only me, but I do know everything that happens round here.'

'I should think that you are enough. Come and sit down and tell me about yourself and there is the slight possibility that I might take you on.'

'I knew that you would not be able to resist having me as a patient.'

'Hang on, Jack. I said there was a slim chance I may take you on.'

'Of course you will.'

'Perhaps you are right. Now, Jack, tell me about yourself. Where do you live?'

'Elftown. It's just a hamlet.'

'I can see why you are small. Are you Head Elf?'

'Of course.'

'Are you married?'

'Yes. My lovely maid Marion.'

'Well, Robin Hood, have you any children?'

'Yes,' he said, 'four boys all living in Canada.'

'Do you get to see them?'

'Of course,' said Jack, 'I walk the Atlantic. No, they are good lads. They come for at least a month a year.'

'Any grandchildren?'

'Yes, fourteen. Some are old enough to come on their own.'

'Hobbies?'

'You sound like the Spanish Inquisition.'

'I am the head of the medical Mafia.'

'Pigeons,' he said. 'I have four lofts and one hundred birds. Two are golden champions – that means they have won a long race.'

'What about your whippet?'

'How do you know about him, Medical Mafia? Yes I have one. I race him on illegal tracks.'

'How can I help you?'

He said, 'It's my skin blemishes.'

'Could I take a look at it?'

'I have to take my trousers off.'

'Okay. Carry on. I've seen that before.'

He took his trousers off.

I said, 'Christ! How did this happen? Did you sit on a box of fireworks?'

'Sort of. I was a coal miner.'

'So was I.'

'Yes, you are a bloody hero; paddy trains, undercut coal, shot firing. A poncy pit,' he said. 'We had to do it tub and stall. It was all pick, shovel and crowbar. Then push your tub up to the main tunnel to be hooked away on an endless chain.'

I said, 'Ours was not that easy.'

'I know,' he said, 'you did well.'

'Now, let's have a look at this burn. Surely this did not happen down the pit?' The whole of the sides of his upper leg were covered in red fibrous tissue; somehow it had missed his genitals. 'How did this happen?'

He said, 'I lived in a miner's cottage and we had a two hole privy at the bottom of the garden. In winter when it was cold and we wanted a shit we used to push a blazing newspaper down the unoccupied hole. On that night there must have been a collection of methane. There was one woosh of flame that came up the toilet hole and got me.'

I said, 'Burnt in action.'

'Yes.'

'Did they not try to graft it?'

'Yes. First guinea pigs' tissue – that made it worse. Then they got twenty teetotal, non-smoking Salvation Army men. They took a piece of flesh about as big as a half crown with a cut out of each one. But like the guinea pig stuff, it just made it worse.'

Jack's legs looked terrible; his thighs were almost fused. The thick fibrous tissue looked like crocodile skin. How on earth he managed to shuffle round on his own, I didn't know. It must have been terribly uncomfortable. 'Jack, it takes courage to go around as you do.'

'I know,' he replied. 'I should have the Victoria Cross but I'll settle by having a crossover on Victoria the barmaid at The George.'

'What a pity they did not try and graft you with goat; it might have taken.'

'You are right, Bob. Is it too late to try?'

'Yes.' I asked what helped him most.

'Roger's tablets.'

'Good. I will give you some more. There are various new ointments that are worth trying. They could soften the skin, and what also might help is hydrotherapy. There is a new one opening in Bath.'

'What's hydrotherapy?'

'You lie in a warm pool and a physiotherapist will come and help you.'

'Are they maids?'

'Yes, ladies.'

'Right, I will. How do I get there? I haven't got a car.'

'I'll fix a hospital car.'

'Tell me, how did the miners treat you?'

'They could not have been kinder. I lived with a collier and his wife and though I was wet behind the ears nobody was ever rude. They took care of me.'

'I expect that was bloody Yorkshire. I would have seen that you got roughed up if you had been down here. Coal miners in Somerset are proper ones, not the poncy ones you worked with.'

'Tell me, as Head Elf, what do you do?'

'I am the local witch doctor. I keep an eye on things, like the lady next door. She had a baby each year for six years then stopped. I said "What's up, Girl?" She said, "It's the NHS." "How the NHS?" "They gave me a hearing aid." What difference did that make?" "Before I got it, when we went to bed at night my husband used to say, Shall we go to sleep or what?"'

'Jack, that's a fib!'

'I know, but you can use the story at a Rotary Lunch.'

'I'm not a Rotarian.'

'You will be.'

I walked with him to the door. 'I have enjoyed your company. I hope when we settle on a house you will come to supper.'

'Khartoum Villa.'

'How did you know that?'

'I did tell you I knew everything. I can always get your wife cheap manure for the garden.'

'She will want to know where the manure came from.'

'Your privy? It could be but it will be expensive as I'll have to get a digger in.' We shook hands.

As he left I said, 'Bottom's up. Jack.'

He replied, 'Bob's your uncle. Goodbye, Uncle.'

As I watched this small man shuffle away I realised what a hugely brave man he was. For at least the last thirty years he, by sheer strength of will, dragged himself around. Every step must have been painful and yet somehow he always seemed to be able to maintain this cheeky sparrow-like demeanour. He became a close personal friend in the years that I knew him. If I could find an excuse I would pop in and see him. I would knock and shout, 'Are you in, Jack Arse?' 'Yes, Uncle,' he would reply, 'come and have a cup of tea.' Marion would make us a cup of tea and we would talk about coal mines and pigeons. I would be the one that had benefited from the visit.

Back in my Surgery, with Jack just gone, I thought it probable that I had kept some patients waiting. I rang for the next and in came a large lady in her late fifties. I said, 'I am sorry to have kept you waiting.'

She snorted. 'You always know you are going to have to wait if Jack is in front of you. I really wanted to see your wife but she is fully booked.'

'I'm sorry. Tell me about yourself.'

'Why should I? That's not your business.'

'How can I help then?'

'I have an itchy bottom. I don't want you to look, just give me some ointment.'

'I have a special one,' I said. 'My grandmother used to use it.'

She replied with, 'Ah.' Then went on, 'I had really come to see if I can help you.'

'Thank you.'

'Why I came was to say that I would babysit for you.'

'We haven't got a baby.'

'But you will have at some stage. What I am saying is that you book me now for whenever it is.'

I said, 'Sorry, but our present plans do not envisage a baby.'

'If that's how it is,' said the stout lady as she got up, 'I have made my offer and it has been turned down. So don't come creeping to me when you are stuck. I will not be available.'

She moved towards the door. She was almost there when I said, 'Just a minute.'

She turned around. 'What's the matter?'

'You have not taken the prescription for your ointment.' I proffered it with my hand.

'Huh!' She snatched it, then she was gone. It was brought home to me that my charm does not always work. I wondered how Priscilla would have got on with her.

My last patient that morning was a distraught woman. When I had been through my usual preamble on where she lived etc., followed by 'How can I help you?' she burst into tears. She said, 'It's my husband. He is an alcoholic. If he was having an affair with another woman I could cope. I cannot compete with drink.'

'Would he come and see me?'

'No. He won't talk about it. He tried Alcoholics Anonymous, but only went the once.'

'There are all sorts of places he could go to for detoxification.'

'It's no good. He won't go anywhere. I am going to leave him and go up north and stay with my sister. I really want something to calm me down and help me to sleep. I hate the thought of leaving here but I can't cope.'

'Of course I can give you something that will help, but only take them for a short time. It is easy to get dependent. The very act of you going could be the thing that brings him to his senses.'

'Do you think so?'

'I think it is a good chance there is little more you can do. I hope it resolves and you are back with us in six months.'

She walked round my desk and kissed me on the cheek. 'You are a good doctor. Thank you.'

You win some, you lose some. My first surgery was over. Of course, it was not my first surgery; I had worked here for four months before our wedding, but it felt different. We had arranged, with the generosity of her time, for Helen to get sandwiches for a working lunch each day. Priscilla was later finishing than I was. She had probably seen twice as many patients as I had. The idea was we had a working lunch where we sorted out visits etc. The faithful Helen was always prepared to field calls for us so if we were out the telephone automatically switched to her. The practice, as it was for Roger, was her baby. I think Roger going almost tore her heart out. She was very sweet with us.

Priscilla was a bit subdued. I was bursting to tell her about Jack Bottom. She smiled as I told my story, but not with the enthusiasm I would have expected.

'What's wrong, my love?'

'Bob, darling, he sounds great. I would love some manure for Christmas, but not the privy stuff. My surgery was not so much fun. I had the most beautiful girl who could be another Ingrid.'

'Hodgkin's Disease?'

She replied, 'I think it could be. She is coming to see me again next week and I would be grateful if we could see her together.'

'It is not necessarily all doom and gloom. I saw in the BMJ an article about a trial. They are having some success. If there is any suggestion she has Hodgkin's we must make sure she gets on the trial. We are geographically well placed for it. Okay. Now here is Helen with the kettle.'

'Helen,' Priscilla queried, 'do we make our own tea?'

'No, there is a case of croup at Sheldon. Dr Roger usually took an electric kettle for croup.'

'I have no experience of croup,' said Priscilla. 'It did not happen in neurology. Why the kettle?'

'Steam. This is the main treatment we can give.'

We shot off, with Priscilla driving, arriving at an address where it sounded as if they had a seal barking. 'Is that a seal I hear?'

'No, that's croup.'

We went into the house where we found a terrified mother holding her two year old who was fighting for her breath and making the seal honk noises.

'Have you hot water in your bathroom?'

'Yes.'

'Go and turn the hot taps on as powerfully as you can, and we need white sheets.'

Somehow, in Priscilla's arms the baby looked calmer. She was not being alarmed by her mother's anxiousness. We made our way to the bathroom. It was already beginning to get steamy. I made a sort of tent with the white sheet, and plugged the kettle in which soon started to steam. I told Priscilla to sit on the toilet lid, and arranged the sheet like a tent with her head the tent pole, with the baby on her lap. I made sure that the kettle spout was aimed into the tent and in five minutes the baby's breath had lost its raucous sound. In ten minutes she was breathing normally.

Listening to the little mite's chest, there were a few squeaks, so I found some liquid antibiotics and wrote some instructions on the bottle. 'Steam is your main weapon,' I told the mother. 'I would keep her in the bathroom for a couple of hours. Have you an electric kettle of your own?'

'Yes.'

'Good. We can rescue ours, otherwise we can't make tea at the surgery.'

The mother was overflowing with thanks. I said, 'Don't hesitate to get in touch if you are worried. That's what we are here for.'

We got back into the car. 'Whew!' Priscilla said. 'Dr

Bob, you were great!'

'So were you,' I replied. 'You can guess how it would have been if I had been on my own. We are a team. I just love us working together. I expect we will have to get a second car at some stage. It would be nice to be able to attend home confinements together.'

When we got back to the surgery Helen made us a cup of tea and the three of us sat down to plan the future of the practice. We were anxious that Helen was in agreement with our suggested plans.

Most of the suggestions we made were greeted by, 'Good. I think that Dr Roger would approve of that.' We would both do a morning surgery each day, except Saturdays when just one of us was on. Monday, Tuesday, Thursday and Friday there would be open evening surgeries, not booked and open until they finished. We would each do two a week; the one of us who was not doing surgery being available as second call and to field any visits that came in. Wednesday afternoons would be an antenatal clinic.

I think Dr Roger would approve of that. Fortunately there was nothing that we suggested that Helen did not accept, always with the rider, 'Dr Roger would approve of that.'

After our belated lunch, we had several home visits to make – most of them routine visits to elderly and disabled people who lived on their own. We and, of course, Dr Roger, used to do it. In the end it saved all sorts of problems and for many of the lonely elderly we were the high point of the week.

One of the disadvantages was that in order to show the patients that they were special, you had to have a cup of tea with them. It could amount to half a dozen cups in an afternoon. We always made our last routine visit of the day to see Mrs. Quincie who was a delight. She was much travelled and told us some amazing stories.

Priscilla was much better that I was in these situations – not that I was particularly bad, patients were fond of me, but they just loved Priscilla. She had this gracious way. She could communicate with people at any level.

As Mrs Quincie was usually the last visit of the day, with six cups of tea on board, I usually had to use her toilet. One day when I was using her facilities she said to Priscilla, 'Is Dr Bob okay? He always seems to be rushing to the toilet.' We could not steal her thunder by saying she was the sixth cup of tea. All the cups of tea givers thought they were special and the only ones. Priscilla said, 'I keep a very close eye on him.'

Mrs Quincie replied, 'He is lucky to have you. I would trust you with my life.'

'I am just as lucky as Dr Bob, I couldn't have a better man.'

'Yes,' said Mrs Quincie, 'but women are stronger than men. I cannot think of anything a man does that could not be better done by a woman, except digging holes in the road.'

'Dr Bob was a coal miner before he became a doctor.'

'That's what I mean,' said Mrs Quincie. 'It is still digging holes, but deeper down.'

By then I was entering the room, making sure that I had adjusted my clothes properly. For some reason, I had omitted to do up my zip. The ever-caring Priscilla said, 'Bob, darling, I think you have some egg on your tie.' I developed a technique of going to a mirror to examine my tie with one hand and surreptitiously pulling up my zip with the other.

We did buy a second car so we no longer went as a pair to our home visits. This cut down on the cups of tea; they almost dried up, though I think Priscilla still had more. Helen said Dr M had her own car when she was in practice with Dr Roger.

We did manage to get to nearly all confinements

together. We took it in turn changing ends at each delivery. We really enjoyed the maternity and the happy ending. We never lost a mother or a baby. Not because we were clever, we antenatalled carefully and really had no problems.

There was a cottage hospital halfway between Plumstock and Bath, which had maternity and surgery facilities with special obstetricians and surgeons on call. So if we had any doubts in our antenatal examination, we would refer them to the specialist obstetricians and sometimes patients referred had to have their babies in hospital under specialist care, which in some cases meant delivery by Caesarean Section.

After we delivered a baby they were taken over by Health Visitors and District Nurses. The next thing we did was to give the poor little mites a smallpox injection. I personally, of course, had never seen smallpox, but thought that treatment was unnecessary.

How wrong I was.

Out of the blue somebody who had been abroad somewhere came back with the highly contagious infection. There were about half a dozen deaths, including two doctor pathologists who did the post mortems. The government ordered general vaccination throughout the UK, so with our practice we would have to vaccinate about 5,000 patients. This did not mean there was a panic, but everyone was quite anxious to have one. So it was all hands to the pumps. I rang my teaching hospital and a couple of students came down to help. The two of us, with our nurses, district nurses and the two students, did 4,964 vaccinations in four days. There were great queues of patients right down the roads to the surgery. Thank God that was the end of smallpox in this country.

We, of course, still had our day to day patients to look after during this giant vaccination spree. I don't remember a quieter time in the practice. I think they were aware of the gravity of the situation. Priscilla and I boxed and coxed our way through surgeries and visits.

We saw the girl who Priscilla thought might have Hodgkin's disease. She was quite poorly when she came to the surgery. Most patients in her condition would have asked for a home visit. Her visit coincided with the arrival of a blood test result that showed she had glandular fever. We were both relieved. The girl herself had a really rough time and it necessitated three months off work, but she was much better off than poor Ingrid.

The two of us worked well as a team. Both of us had areas of specialist knowledge of various diseases and conditions. This was the pattern of our lives. Come the winter I tried to do most of the out of hours visits, but Priscilla would have none of it and she insisted that we did it fifty-fifty. Out of bed calls we went together.

I always took the precaution of carrying a piece of lead pipe, not to protect us against people, but dogs. A tap on the nose saved us from being bitten. We would hear a call from the patient, 'Just ignore the dog.' We were happy to do that. But too often, large protective dogs had a different point of view.

Once there was a night call that dealt with faecal compaction. Priscilla did not put up a fight. Faecal compaction meant bowel obstructed by constipation. There was only one treatment when enemas had failed. You literally had to roll up your sleeves, put on a pair of rubber gloves and dig them out. I always made sure that there was plenty of newspaper spread round the room. However long you were in practice, even if you were the snappiest dresser in the county, from time to time you would have to roll up your sleeves.

Priscilla came into her own with babies and young children. She could just communicate. I was a Calpol and Gripe Water man; if I had any doubt or problem, I would call her in. Her elegant and gracious assurance seemed to spread calm through the situation, not only reassuring mother and child, but me as well. I seemed to get on best with old ladies, and got away with saying the most outrageous things to them. An 'Oh, doctor, that was awful' meant they loved it, particularly if it was a bit naughty.

Priscilla was always surprising me. One evening after supper, I was reading a book by my favourite author, the Pulitzer Prize winner, J. P. Marquand, when Priscilla said, 'I ought to get back to my quilting.'

'What's quilting?'

'Making quilts.'

'You don't have to make one, my love, we can always buy one.'

'Never ever like this one,' she replied. She went and fetched a sewing machine, and a box that had a sheet of embroidery of different coloured squares on it. About half the squares had beautiful embroidered pictures on them.

'Did you do all this?'

'Yes. What else can a lonely girl on her own for seven years do?'

The quilt was like a diary; the first embroidered square was Boyston Hall with a baby and a little boy in one corner. Presumably the birth of Priscilla. I scanned through the other finished embroidered squares. There was obviously school days, holidays, then about three quarters through my scan I found a picture of a rugby player. I said, 'When was this one done?'

She looked at the back then said, '1947.'

We had met by then.

'Yes, it's you. I did that just after the Hospital Cup.'

'Is that me?'

'Of course it's you, idiot!'

'But I haven't got a moustache.'

'You haven't there, it is just where the thread has fluffed up.'

'How lovely. Please come over and give me a kiss, I feel overwhelmed.'

'Okay,' she replied. 'If you will come and thread my needle for me.'

'Any time,' I replied. I was overwhelmed by all the effort and skills that she had put into this beautiful quilt. It made me realise how little, in fact, we knew about each other. We knew from first sight that we loved each other to bits. But life had been such a whirlwind since New Year's Eve. I tended to be all shop front, so there was no rabbit I would pull out of a hat. Priscilla had huge unknown areas I knew nothing about. I was so lucky. As Jack Bottom once said after he and Marion had been round for a meal, 'Bob, she is perfect. How on earth did she land up with a Yorkshire ponce like you?'

'That's easy,' I replied. 'She knows that I am in touch with the head of the local Mafia.'

'Spot on!'

'Now use the inside toilet tonight. Give the privy a miss.'

'Okay, Uncle. Thank you from both of us for a lovely evening.'

One day, Priscilla said, 'I hope you don't mind – I have invited someone for the night.'

'No, of course not. Is it someone I know?'

'I don't think you do. She is Lily Mills, and she is six months old and teething. Her mother, Emma, has not slept for a couple of weeks and is at the end of her tether. I said we would give her a break.'

'That's fine,' I replied.

We went to the council estate called Paradise Way to pick up this screaming baby from a pale and exhausted mother.

As we drove home, I said, 'I have plenty of Calpol.'

'Let's see how we go. I think she is hungry.'

Already in Priscilla's arms the baby was much calmer. When we got home I nursed the baby while she made up a bottle of milk. Of course, as soon as I held the baby she started to scream again. I was pleased to hand her over as soon as the milk was ready. She devoured it, then fell fast asleep. We had arranged a cot beside our bed and apart from waking up once, when she was given more milk, she slept soundly until breakfast time. When she had had even more milk, we drove her back to her mother before morning surgery, to find she looked like a normal person as opposed to a ghost. She was profuse with her thanks. 'Is there anything I can do for you, Doctor Ramsden?'

'Who knows? It could be me asking you for help in the future.'

As we drove to the surgery, I said, 'I am so proud of you, my love.'

'Darling, Bob, let's not go down that route. We are P and B Ramsden, Family Doctors, and what we have just done is, in my book, what family doctors do.'

This began the pattern of our life. We really worked hard together, but it was not all work. We were very fortunate that we always had Roger in the background to stand in for us when needed. We took up all the invitations of the surrounding practices, making sure we did not get too involved with people. Our favourite company was our own. It took us six months to get everything sorted out with Khartoum Villa; furniture from family and friends, particularly Miles. He almost completely furnished the place.

My father said, 'Don't refuse anything anyone offers you, even if you don't really want it. If you refuse something, whoever offered it will not offer you anything again.'

In the August after we got back, we went up to Boyston Hall for Mark and Gillian's wedding, which was much on the same lines as ours. The morning after their Wedding Breakfast we were still in bed. It had been a late evening. The chapel clock struck ten. Priscilla nudged me. She said, 'Maud will be taking in the tray about now.'

'I hope that they are not compromised.'

'I think it unlikely. I think they jumped the gun a few months ago.'

From time to time we went on holiday with Mark and Gillian and Joyda and Irene. My best friends were Joyda and Mark. Priscilla and Gillian were the sisters that neither of them had. Gillian was not as good-looking as Priscilla. She was a bit shorter, with auburn hair and a wonderful sense of humour. Mark, of course, thought that she was much better looking than his younger sister.

At Khartoum Villa, we loved to sit under the porch, with its wide opening and view of the Somerset Levels, where we could see the starlings swirling. One of the first things we did was to plant a wisteria in the middle of the opening of the porch hoping that in the future it might start to fill it with beautiful blue blossom.

Work in the practice steadily increased as the number of patients grew. After three years it had doubled in size. This was not because of our personal magnetism and medical skills, although it probably played some part. This new inflow of patients was mainly caused by a massive building project to the east of Plumstock, mostly of affordable housing, which was good for first time buyers, with some facilities for sheltered accommodation for older people. The balance was mainly for the young, but with enough older residents so there were a few people available for such things as dog walking and babysitting.

We had to take in some help and our advertisement

for a partner had a massive response. The first applicant we interviewed turned up with his wife, also a doctor. We liked them both immensely and we took both on as new partners. They started out in the locum's flat, as we had.

EPILOGUE

Joe and Susan Wainwright were all we could have possibly wished for. They had come through their hospital resident posts, as we had. They had married as students; their rationale was that if they had waited until they could afford to, it probably would never have happened. The locum's flat was the first accommodation they had shared, just like us. Priscilla had stocked up the flat, just as Molly Ross had done for us.

Having four of us as partners when we really probably could have managed with three, or three-and-a-half, meant that our workload was reduced and we could take the opportunity of having six weeks holiday a year.

Once they were firmly settled in, we took off for four weeks touring on the continent. What we enjoyed most was each other. We had such fun and a great deal of loving. We went to Ghent to see the Van Eyck polyptych of The Holy Lamb of Ghent. I had always promised we would. It was an incredible piece of work. As we looked at it I said to Priscilla, 'I wonder how different things would have been if we had not gone to the Royal

Institution to hear the lecture about this?'

'It would have been exactly the same. I had you in my sights, I wasn't going to lose you and I was going to, as a last resort if necessary, propose to you myself, which of course I did in the end.'

We came back to Khartoum Villa and settled into the community. I, of course, became a committee member of the Plumstock Rugby Club, eventually over the years rising to become president, and a member of the Rotary but, although often invited to stand, I never fancied going on the council.

Similarly Priscilla, after first serving on the committee of the riding club, eventually becoming the president. She was a Commissioner in the Girl Guides and we were both officers of the Red Cross and St John's Ambulance.

Very occasionally we would go into Bath to the cinema. We went to see the film of Thomas Hardy's book *Far From the Madding Crowd*. The film, which I thought was excellent, was proceeding fine when Priscilla gripped my hand so tightly that I turned to see she had tears running down her face. We had just watched the scene when Gabriel proposes saying, 'When I look up, there will be thee, and when thee looks up, there will be I.'

'Bob,' she said, 'that's how we are. How did Thomas Hardy know?'

I said, 'He was a very learned and wise man. What he said was written, as you know, many, many years ago. I remember that literary quote which I heard from Christopher Fry, and told you at my father's on New Year's Day. The sensation of overtaking something that has always been waiting for you.'

'I remember. Darling, I want to cling to you.'

'We can't in here.' There were already mutterings from the people sitting behind us. 'Let's go.' I was still conscious of Priscilla almost desperately squeezing my hand. We got to the foyer where people were already queuing for the next performance and I said, 'We can't cling together here. There is a park across the road. We can go there.'

'Can we make love there?'

'That would not be a good idea, we might draw a crowd.'

As we drove home I realised how upset she was. It was the first time I had ever seen her close to losing her composure. She said, 'I am so sorry but hearing someone say those particular words, I felt as if my personal space had been invaded. I thought the words spoken were private to you and me. I had the feeling that as they spoke, everybody would turn and look at us.'

'Darling,' I replied, 'it is private to us. All words are just words, only you and I have our own intimate language. I have a copy of the book at home, we could read it together on the sofa, or I could take you to bed and really invade your personal space.'

She laughed out loud. 'Oh darling Bob, you always seem to be able to put things right.' She was herself again. 'I am quicker than you are up the stairs, so when we get in I will race up to the bedroom before you and will be waiting for you. Darling, I do hate to criticise, do you realise that you are driving at ninety-five miles an hour. I don't think it's allowed.'

'Oh my God!' I slowed down to fifty.

As soon as we got home she rushed upstairs as promised and made love more passionately than she ever had before, sobbing as we clung together. 'Are you alright, my love?' I asked.

'Absolutely fine. Bob, I am so lucky to have you.'

I said, 'I know someone who is even luckier.'

'Impossible.'

'No, it isn't. It's me having you. I have an idea. It's something quite daring that we said we would never do.'

'Okay. I am game for anything. What is it?'

'If we buy a television set we can watch it, or not watch it, whenever we like, and we could keep it in the bedroom.'

'No, it would not be good for the children. We will have to get two sets.'

'Which children?' Then it dawned on me that this new emotion might have a basis and the phrase 'under the influence of pregnancy and lactation' came to mind. 'Are you pregnant?'

'I think so. I think it must have been the night after we saw the polyptych.'

'Darling,' I said, 'this is wonderful news. That's tremendous. I can hardly take it in. Are you taking enough rest? Are you eating properly? I ought to leave you alone for the next few months.'

'Don't you dare. It is very good exercise for me.'

'You must cut down on work. We have Joe and Sue now.'

'I'm fine,' she said, 'please don't worry my love. I am sorry about my behaviour in the cinema. It wasn't me.'

'I quite understand pregnancy and lactation – you are allowed to kill someone and get away with it if you want to.'

'It's okay, I have no desire to kill anyone. I am so pleased we have created something between us.'

'One more person to cherish. When the baby is born can we call it Polyptych Ramsden?'

'Certainly not! If it's a girl I don't mind if she is called Penelope.'

I had always enjoyed my midwifery; it was hands on stuff that I was good at and more than any other branch of medicine, there was practically always a happy ending. I was the calm, reassuring obstetrician confirmed with the title of DRCOG (Diploma in

Obstetrics and Gynaecology). I was able to reassure worrying fathers and was confident enough in my own abilities to sit and watch, and let nature take its course. That is until Priscilla became pregnant, when I found I was leading the pack of worrying fathers-to-be. I started to read up all the complications of childbirth, coming up with situations I had never met or even heard of, which of course, I added to my worry pile.

Sue, our new partner, was to deliver the baby at home, helped by our excellent midwife, Nurse Wood. I watched Priscilla like a hawk in spite of the excellent antenatal care of Sue and Nurse Wood. I was constantly examining her myself. I would have taken her blood pressure three times a day if she had let me.

She became as near to being cross with me than she had ever been. 'Bob dear, do stop worrying. You will come home one day and you will find me and baby waiting for you.'

'No! No!' I said. 'I want to be there at the birth.'

'Fine,' said Priscilla, 'but if you become a nuisance I will throw you out. My love, I'm fine and everything is going to be alright.'

She would have worked until she went into labour but I insisted that she gave up work at six months. Even though she had an increasingly large stomach she still always looked elegant. Miles came down to stay for a couple of days and in spite of all his years with a stiff upper lip seemed as anxious as I was, to the extent that Priscilla said, 'Go out and have a lads' night out.' So we did and both had too much to drink.

When Miles went back, I just had to keep worrying on my own. When Priscilla started to have labour pains, my worrying reached its peak. This of course meant Joe and I were the only two working. I was just coming in and out.

'Bob dear, please stop worrying. If I was in India, all I

would do is have baby at the side of the field then go back to work picking cotton or whatever they do.'

I said, 'No cotton picking today. It will be some time before you are going to deliver, so I will get done what visits I have to, then I shall be back for the delivery. I do want to be here for the delivery of my first born.'

Fortunately my visits did not take long, so I was back earlier than I expected. I walked into the room to find Priscilla nursing the baby and the placenta safely in a kidney dish.

'Penelope,' said Priscilla, 'meet your daddy.'

I picked up this precious bundle. Although I had delivered many babies, for the first time I realised what a joy it is to have your own. 'What happened? I so wanted to be here for the delivery.'

'I know,' said Sue. 'You didn't trust us. She just popped out, beyond our control.'

In fact I was so relieved I hadn't been there, as I am sure I would have been a nuisance.

Although baby was christened Penelope, for some reason she was called Poppy, and it was not related to her delivery. It so happened that having advised so many people on baby care, with my own baby I was a dead loss. If she cried I wondered what was wrong and if she wasn't crying I would be crouched over her cot wondering if she was still breathing.

In spite of me, she thrived. It was a joy to see her develop; her fingers clutching my finger and, of course, Priscilla breast fed her. It was a picture to see mother and baby together. I just adored this little scrap and was always trying to nip back home to see her. It was the first time I had watched a baby develop. When she was six months old I took her swimming. She loved it.

Once we found a nanny, Priscilla was prepared to go back to work immediately. I insisted that she waited for six months, but she was back in four. Poppy's birth produced the same sort of reaction as our wedding. Presents from patients to Priscilla and baby came pouring in. I think there were enough for us to open a baby care shop.

Eventually, Poppy went on to be a top Shakespearean actress. She was always known as Poppy Ramsden; her career lasted about seven years, then she met a solicitor called David Wallace, married him and gave up the stage and produced three grandchildren for us.

Two years after Poppy was born, Miles arrived – an eight-pound lusty boy who in time took up medicine and became a physician, marrying a nurse and, as if to beat Poppy, produced four more grandchildren.

Our third and last child was another girl who we called Jane. She certainly wasn't a 'plain Jane'. She was the nearest to having looks like her mother than anybody else. She took up nursing and was almost nun-like in her attitude to life. She never married and would go nursing to impoverished and troublesome areas; orphanages and hospitals mainly in Africa, India and Asia. She was always graceful and elegant and carried an aura of calm tranquillity about her, which on its own so often could diffuse problems by her just being there.

When it had been confirmed that Poppy was on the way, we had built a self-contained annex on to Khartoum Villa to house a nanny help, Gladys, who remained with us until the children were teenagers. Then unexpectedly she went off to get married and sadly completely disappeared from our lives.

Mark and Gillian had four children, and children's parties were absolute riots. The cousins all loved to play together and had good age matches. Joyda and Irene, who were almost family, had two children. He said, 'We believe in quality not quantity. You bloody English are like rabbits!'

In later years when Priscilla and I looked back, we

thought that some of the happiest times of our lives were holidays with the children. We went camping all over France, Wales and Scotland. We had holidays on canal boats and various trips to London. We had such fun. It was really my chance to bond with them as being a very busy GP, I used to work round the clock.

Pregnancies, of course, limited the amount of time that Priscilla could spend practising medicine. She began to take a great interest in gardening at the villa. The garden was terraced with a patio in front of the porch where the wisteria was really coming on well. In front of this was a wide patio with potted plants, and trees and shrubs at the side. Below this was the upper lawn, then a dry stone wall down to the lower lawn where there was a pond and summer house, and which was our favourite barbecue area.

Each layer of the terraces had flowerbeds, and at the end of the bottom lawn was a row of shrubs, magnolias, camellias, and azalea. In May and June it was an absolute picture. 'In an English Country Garden.' At the back of the house was a greenhouse and a large vegetable plot. Priscilla almost kept us in vegetables and fruit in the summer. There was a conveyor belt of tomatoes and cucumber.

Priscilla's sister-in-law Gillian was at least her equal in gardening. They were both almost gardening addicts. They were often off together to see flower shows and gardening centres. Gillian really transformed the gardens at Boyston Hall and Mark made a great success of the family business, buying more land and upgrading their existing farms. He was, like his father, a complete gentleman through and through. He took the greatest care of his employees and they in turn loved him. He had Boyston Hall refurbished until it was literally gleaming. Being the complete businessman, he decided to open the garden and hall to the public.

It was about now that Miles senior's health, which of course was compatible with his age, deteriorated. I was never sure whether he came to live with us because he wanted two doctors to look after him in his declining years or whether it was because the precious family home was open to the public. I expect it was a bit of both.

He lived in the extension that we had built for Gladys, adding on an extra room to house his precious sketches. There was a complete love affair between him and the grandchildren. He knew just how to talk to them. He also knew the right sort of games.

I enjoyed having Miles around; I loved to hear him talk about his days in the Army, particularly in India where he was present at the era of the Raj, but he never talked about Arnhem.

He would potter round the garden trying to help Priscilla as much as he could. Sadly, and eventually, he declined, as we all do, and passed away in his ninetieth year. His body was taken up to be buried next to his wife at Boyston Hall.

Similarly my father and Louise, in declining years, moved from their lovely flat to a very expensive nursing home. They, like Miles, inevitably passed away, fortunately within the same fortnight, at a similar age to Miles.

Priscilla and I never tired of each other; our love never wavered. Life was not a bed of roses. We both, fortunately at different times, had life threatening medical conditions. Priscilla was put right by surgery. I had both surgery and rather devastating chemotherapy. The only positive thing I had from my chemotherapy, apart from curing me of course, was that during the process of having it, I met the finest and most dedicated doctors and nurses that I had ever met in my medical life and to whom I was extremely grateful.

We, like all the rest of the world, had our problems: getting babies established with breast-feeding; bed-wetting; getting them embedded in schools; acne; tears; tantrums; love affairs; marriage, then of course our much loved grandchildren.

Both Priscilla and I retired from medicine in our early sixties. I took up fishing and fulfilled a longed-for ambition of doing some writing about the countryside and fishing, and Priscilla helped me write about gardening for countryside magazines. She continued with her gardening. I made my contribution by paying a gardener to help her with the heavy work a couple of days a week.

As we sit in the porch, which is now filled with blue wisteria blossom, looking down we can see the grandchildren, or is it the great grandchildren, as both lots call me 'Grandpa'. It makes little difference. They are all chasing each other round the pond.

When I say 'all', that is all except one, the smallest. For some reason he was christened Alfred; why, I don't know, as of course everyone calls him 'Fred'. Now Fred is about four and my favourite – I know you shouldn't, but I have broken all my rules and he is mine. He came fishing with me three times and just sat quietly and contentedly by me. We caught nothing on the first two trips. On the third I landed a fine brown trout. I thought he was going to burst with excitement.

Now, as the others run around, he is sitting on a small stool fishing. His equipment consists of a bamboo stick with a piece of string attached; the other end of the string being attached to an open safety pin. The needle part is baited with a piece of bread. Although we have explained to him that there are not actually any fish in the pond, he sits stoically on. He is going to catch a fish, like Grandpa. Oh how I wish I could stay alive for long enough to see this little boy grow up, but, of course, I won't.

As I look across at Priscilla, to me she looks as beautiful as she did on the first day I saw her. She says that is the only beneficial effect of my deteriorating vision. Alas, I am no longer a 'muscular man'.

We are both now in our early eighties. I should perhaps have stopped writing our story after we became engaged that New Year's Eve so many years ago, but I wanted to show that people can live happily ever after and live long and fulfilled lives.

THE END

Printed in Great Britain
by Amazon.co.uk, Ltd.,
Marston Gate.